WHEN MEN HAD TIME TO LOVE

WHEN MEN HAD TIME TO LOVE

Agnes de Stoeckl and Wilfrid S. Edwards

JOHN MURRAY

Dedicated by gracious permission to
Her Majesty Queen Victoria Eugenie of Spain
God-daughter of the Empress Eugénie

First published 1953
This edition 1968

*Printed in Great Britain for
John Murray, Albemarle Street, London
by Cox & Wyman Ltd, London, Reading
and Fakenham*

CONTENTS

PART ONE

PART TWO

FOREWORD

It would be presumptuous to endeavour to compete with the famous authors who have written so brilliantly of the life of the Empress Eugénie.

I shall, however, attempt to depict scenes which were described to me by personages who surrounded her.

After the death of the Prince Imperial we shall leave the Empress for a while to continue the picture of the city she loved so well, a city to which she brought laughter and light.

Although the Imperial Eagles had vanished, the impulse given by the Empress was not stayed until the lights went out.

1826

Granada has been shaken by an earthquake, many houses shattered, and the people, fearing further shocks, are encamped in their gardens.

The first rays of the rising sun fall softly through the seams of a tent pitched under the trees, they kiss the face of a new-born babe.

Awakened by their warm caress, her eyes open widely.

How lovely those clear blue eyes, how enchanting that first faint smile of Eugénie, the babe born to fulfil a gipsy forecast: 'You will be a Queen and you will live a hundred years.'

PART ONE

1 LA CABALE MONTIJO

The clock is just striking eleven on the morning of 13th January in the year 1853, as Eugénie de Montijo turns the handle of the door of her mother's boudoir, at Numéro 12, Place Vendôme.

Eugénie looks radiant in her white satin *négligé*, as she moves towards the log fire burning brightly in the grate.

Resting one tiny foot on the brass fender rail, she glances at the clock and with a slight gesture of impatience lightly taps her fingers on the marble mantelpiece.

Raising her eyes, she looks into the mirror, but her mind is filled with such a medley of conflicting emotions that she scarcely sees her reflection.

In a few moments her fate will be sealed.

Her mother's advice and her own intrigues have won the day.

It is a triumph, but she wonders if the Crown of France is brilliant enough to blind her eyes to the enigmatical personality of the man she will have to accept as her husband.

Last night at the State Ball at the Tuileries, she and her mother had faced humiliation, public humiliation.

As they approached the seats to the left of the Throne, Madame Drouyn de Lhuys, wife of the Foreign Minister, had proclaimed in a loud voice:

'These are reserved for high officials.'

They had hesitated and were about to withdraw, when the Emperor himself stepped down from the dais, and, taking Eugénie by the hand, had led them to the gilt chairs amidst the Imperial Family.

Even after that, things had not been so easy.

She had determined to bring Napoleon to the point of making his decision that night. As she danced with him, she had whispered:

'Sire! I wish to speak to you in private.'

Quickly he replied, 'Come tomorrow.'

'No, Sire, it must be tonight. I wish to say good-bye.'

Napoleon had looked at her with an expression of astonishment and dismay. Drawing her aside from the crowd of dancers, he led her to the Louis XIV Salon that he used as his private study, and, in a voice almost trembling with emotion, he said:

'Why farewell?'

Eugénie recalled how calm she had become as she staked her fortune in one desperate sentence.

'Sire! I will not remain to be insulted by your Court.'

Napoleon had understood at once, and even now she felt the relief with which her fears were swept away by his instant reply.

'You will never be insulted again; tomorrow I shall ask the Comtesse de Montijo for the honour of your hand.'

'Tomorrow is a long way off; there may be objections tomorrow: I suggest, Sire, that you write a letter to my mother tonight.'

She had felt a pang of guilt as she had pressed the point home, but she knew that a promise written, was more difficult to break.

Without a moment's hesitation, the Emperor had seated himself at his writing table, written the fateful note and summoned Monsieur Mocquard, his *Chef de Cabinet*; Eugénie watching the latter's face, had seen the astonishment with which he had received the command.

'Take this yourself tomorrow morning to the Comtesse de Montijo.'

She recalled each event of that momentous evening, savouring her emotions as each detail was reviewed.

Suddenly the door opens, and Madame de Montijo enters followed by her Spanish maid, Pepa.

'No letter yet! How did you sleep, Eugénie? As for me, I never closed my eyes!'

Pepa lays the tray with two cups of chocolate on a small table, which she places near the fire.

As usual she is grumbling in her familiar way.

'As for me, I have had enough of Paris. It is all tinsel and sham; the only place where the Senorita will find a decent husband is Madrid.'

At this moment the bell of the front door peals loudly, the two ladies look at each other in silence, then there is a knock on the door of the boudoir, and the butler enters:

'Monsieur Mocquard, with a letter from His Majesty the Emperor, which he wishes to hand to Madame la Comtesse in person.'

As the servant retires, closing the door behind him, Madame de Montijo takes her daughter in her arms.

'At last, my child! Eugénie, Empress of the French!'

The days have passed swiftly, and it is now a week later, the evening of 20th January, 1853

In a carriage drawn by high stepping horses sits the Comte de Morny, who is taking the young Prince de Reuss to dine with Alice Howard.

The Prince has not, as yet, met her, so as they drive, he asks Morny to tell him something of this famous personality.

'What can I tell you, *mon Prince*, except that she is a remarkable woman, more beautiful than most and certainly extremely astute. I am told her origin was humble, much resembling that of Nelson's lady love, Lady Hamilton.

'She was very young when she began her career, but unlike my compatriots who live but for the moment careless of the future, she has managed to attract riches and to retain them.

'Lady Blessington protected her, and, I think, managed to marry her to a certain Major Martin, but the union did not last long.

'She lived at Rockingham House, St. John's Wood, in London. There it was that Napoleon met her and was bewitched. She became his mistress, and it was she who financed his enterprise.

'I sincerely believe that of all his *amourettes* she is the only one to retain his affection – but, enough, here we are, and you, *mon ami*, will be able to judge for yourself what a beautiful English-woman can be like.'

The guests are gathering in the handsome mansion in the rue de Cirque where Alice Howard is giving a dinner party.

Rows of footmen in liveries designed by the fair owner of the house, stand waiting to take the capes, top hats and canes, as the carriages drive up.

Only men are invited tonight; as they greet one another, none speak of the one topic that has been circulating for the past eight

11

days, and which is uppermost in every mind – the rumour of the engagement of the Emperor to Eugénie de Montijo.

As they enter the long vista of reception rooms, they are conscious of a discordant note in the decor; a mixture of Empire furniture and English comfort.

Green satin curtains woven with the Imperial bees, tables and bookcases heavily encrusted with finely wrought bronze, Aubusson carpets, and in the midst of all this, English arm-chairs.

Suddenly, the doors are flung open and their hostess appears. She is very lovely in a black velvet gown, her only jewels a *rivière* of flawless diamonds.

Comte Walewski, the Duc de Persigny, Comte de Fleury, and Morny advance to kiss her hand, and the others follow.

Although she is fully thirty-five, years seem to mean nothing. As she stands there, exchanging a few words of welcome with her guests, the charm which had captivated Napoleon flows around her. Dinner is announced, and she leads the way to the dining-room. When all are seated, there is seen to be one vacant chair.

Who is the unlucky man who thus dares the wrath of her incomparable chef?

It appears that the culprit is an attaché of the British Embassy, recently appointed, young, inexperienced, and very full of his own newly acquired importance.

There is a stir at the door, the young man enters with many apologies. He explains to his hostess that he has been unavoidably detained at the Embassy. The news had just been conveyed to the Ambassador of the engagement of the Emperor, Napoleon III, to Mlle de Montijo.

There is a silence which seems to be almost endless; the guests glance sidelong at Napoleon's mistress. Then, showing no sign of the emotion she must feel, Alice Howard slowly raises her glass of champagne and says simply:

'I drink to their happiness.'

The same night, a few hours later, and not very far away, another party is assembling.

Many of the men who have dined with Alice Howard have found their way here, to spend a gay hour in the house of the famous *demi-mondaine*, Adèle Courtois.

Amongst the company already assembled are the notorious Leonide le Blanc, Anna Deslion, Caroline Letessier, and Isabelle Ferand.

The conversation is lively and the stories distinctly *risqués*; here too the rumours so intriguing to Paris, are being discussed rather broadly.

When the men arrive, the ladies rise *en masse* exclaiming excitedly:

'Is it true what we have heard?'

The Comte de Morny makes a sign of assent, at which, with one accord, the whole party throw themselves on their guests, and begin waltzing wildly round the room, whilst one sits down at the piano. The music grows faster and faster till pandemonium itself seems let loose.

More and more men arrive as the evening wears on, to be joined by other well-known *cocottes*.

When the revelry is at its height, Adèle jumps up on to one of the gilt tables, raising her glass of champagne high in the air, she cries at the top of her voice to make herself heard above the din:

'Now we can look forward to days of Life, Love and Laughter and, above all, Money.'

There is a shout of applause from all the women, the men were not quite so enthusiastic.

The night life of Paris is thronging the boulevards, indeed, tonight the pavements and cafés seem even more crowded than usual, as groups of smart clubmen enter the Café de Paris.

The great news has now been released, and so exciting is it that none seems to notice the bright lights which cast their glare into the dark street, outlining the branches of the gaunt and leafless trees, and revealing the tattered figures of the beggars, who cluster in the shadows near the great doors of the famous restaurant.

Everyone is too preoccupied with the announcement, and is wondering just how the news will benefit him; selfishly perhaps, but it is the universal thought in every mind.

The *maître d'hôtel* seems to be everywhere at once – consulting with the *chef de cuisine*, bustling the black-coated *garçons*, and storming at the white-aproned *plongeurs*.

The tables are gleaming with silver, waiters rush hither and thither, dishes held high in their hands; champagne corks pop, and there is a buzz of excited conversation, as men in immaculate evening dress pass from table to table pausing at times to discuss the vital topic of the moment, the engagement of the Emperor and Eugénie.

'*Au fond*,' some would muse, 'it is not much of a match, probably a great mistake politically, *mais après tout* doubtless it might prove an amusing episode.'

The same evening, the curtain has just fallen on the last act of *Phèdre*, at the Théâtre Français, the audience is dispersing, and the artistes' foyer is filling with people

The *abonnés* are arriving, some laden with flowers, but many carrying intriguing shaped leather cases, obviously containing jewels, diamond bracelets, necklaces and even heirlooms, mere trifles, costing a fortune designed to satisfy for the nonce the rapacity of their mistresses.

Passing through the room, it is evident that, here again, the same theme is the subject of every conversation.

Suddenly Rachel appears in the doorway, her rapid rise to fame has astonished the Capital. Gaunt and thin, but exquisitely dressed, she surveys the assembly; it is evident that as yet she has heard nothing.

Laughingly she inquires:

'Why all these mysterious whispers?'

'*L'Empereur épouse La Montijo*,' is the reply.

Rachel looks around, and then bursts into laughter.

'*En voilà un qui sera bientôt cocu!*' she shouts.

In a totally different milieu, in her brilliantly lit mansion, 24 rue de Courcelles, Princesse Mathilde, Comtesse Paul Demidoff, Princesse de San Donato, recently created Imperial Highness by the Emperor, is holding one of her weekly receptions. Ambassadors, academicians, men of letters and several of the newly created Dukes and Princes, have come to pay homage to the celebrated hostess.

How rapidly the vision of Empire has passed from a dream of phantasy to the realm of reality.

It was not so long ago, in September 1848, to be exact, whilst

Princesse Mathilde was in Dieppe enjoying the delights of sea-bathing – then just coming to be a fashionable pastime – that her cousin Louis Napoleon arrived in Paris and engaged rooms at the Hôtel du Rhin, in the Place Vendôme.

This marked the end of his thirty-four years of exile.

He was barely eight when he was forced to leave the country with his mother, La Reine Hortense of Holland; he had returned twice it is true, but each time only to become a prisoner of State. Now, although he knew practically nobody of note, he was fully determined to make a name for himself.

The financial aid that he had received from his mistress, Alice Howard, had been exhausted, now he turned for assistance to the woman, whom, many years before he had hoped to marry, his cousin Mathilde.

Her father, Jerome, King of Westphalia, brother of Napoleon I, had spurned this young adventurer, as he had termed him, and although Queen Hortense had done her best to foster the match, it had come to nothing.

He asked Mathilde to meet him in Paris. She came, and he explained that money was urgently needed to finance his political campaign. With that impetuous generosity, so characteristic of her, she pawned her jewels, and it was a large sum of money that she was able to pass on for his use.

In rapid succession, Napoleon became first, Deputé, then Prince President. She was repaid a hundredfold, and became his official hostess at the Palais de l'Élysée.

After the *coup d'état*, Napoleon, now an Emperor reigning from the Tuileries, had said:

'As long as there is no Empress, you, my cousin, will always pass first, and sit at my right hand.'

So, this evening, Princess Mathilde receives her guests, dressed in a wide crinoline gown of dark red satin, the low bodice outlined with rubies and diamonds; six rows of pearls fall loosely round her handsome neck; her hair dressed in soft bandeaux, and crowned by a head-dress of lace and ribbon, almost hidden by diamond stars and pearl-headed pins which stand out like spikes from her coiffure.

She sits there on a gilt arm-chair, her perfect profile outlined against the olive green *lambris* of the walls.

15

The Comte de Nieuwekerke stands near, as her Cavalier-in-chief, handsome, tall and distinguished – truly it is an Imperial picture.

Her salon is noted for its unique tone of culture and intellect, as much as for the fame of the men and women who frequent it.

It is truly said, 'that she could not be bored by stupid people'.

Her temperament is quick, and not always easy: sometimes her anger rises and woe to anyone who opposes her will.

Tonight her rooms are filled to overflowing, perhaps her guests have come in the hope of getting at the truth of the rumour.

Comte Walewski draws near to Nieuwekerke and whispers in his ear.

Nieuwekerke raises his eyebrows, then he approaches the Princesse and speaks to her in a subdued voice, inaudible to even the nearest.

She flushes, and suddenly she seems to lose her head: in tones loud enough to be heard by all in the room, she almost hisses her reply.

'My brother Jerome was right when he said, "One can admire the Montijo, but one does not marry her!"

'For myself, I do not care, L'Empereur has made his decision and must abide the result, but it is crazy! However, what can you expect of a man who never loses his temper and whose greatest sign of annoyance is to say: "It is absurd." '

One or two men standing near, try to appease her, but in vain, and she continues:

'If I had married him, it seems to me that long before this, I should have smashed his head open to see what it contained.'

At last she masters her temper, regains control of herself and begins to laugh.

'Perhaps I exaggerate, and I am only annoyed because, henceforth, I shall have to walk behind Mlle de Montijo.'

2 THE HOLY SAPPHIRES

Few authors have conveyed to the public, perhaps they never knew, the depth of melancholy which overshadowed the character of Eugénie from her early childhood.

It was a sadness which grew, as sorrow upon sorrow overwhelmed her during her long life.

It may be supposed that in those early childish days, she scarcely sensed the atmosphere around her, but as she grew older, she became painfully aware of the love which her mother showered upon Paca, her elder sister, and of the uncalled for severity with which she herself was treated.

Eugénie never resented the preference given to Paca, because she loved her above everyone else.

It was her lot in life always to give more than she received. Paca was fond of Eugénie, but was far too indolent by nature to respond to her constant demands for affection: whilst Eugénie never ceased expressing by word and deed her untiring, almost exalted love for Paca.

As her letters prove, Eugénie wrote to her over and over again, begging for just a brief word of reassurance on one subject after another. She was ever anxious concerning her sister's health – but it is evident that she received few letters in reply.

This helps to explain Eugénie's unconscious craving for affection from those by whom she was surrounded, a craving which was never satisfied.

Monsieur Hanotaux in the preface to *Les Lettres familières de l'Impératrice Eugénie* draws attention to the fact that the Duke of Alba was deeply attracted to both sisters and there is no doubt whatever that Eugénie was very attracted to him, but the Comtesse de Montijo was determined that her eldest daughter should become the Duchess and she brought all her influence to bear upon the Duke, with the result that he became the husband of Paca.

The following letter from Eugénie to her future brother-in-law shows the state of her mind at the time. Although she does

17

not actually name him, one can read between the lines that she loves him and though willing to give him up to her sister, she cannot resist telling him so.

In this letter she also refers to the manner in which her mother treats her.

Madrid
Wednesday evening.
16th May, 1843.

TO THE DUKE OF ALBA.

MY VERY DEAR COUSIN,

You will think it curious that I should write you a letter like this, but there is an end to all things in this world and my end draws near.

I wish to explain to you, all that is in my heart, it is more than I can endure.

It is true my character is strong and I do not wish to excuse my behaviour, but on the other hand, when one is good to me, I would do anything they want, but when I am treated like a donkey and beaten before people, it is more than I can bear: my blood boils and I cease to know what I am doing.

Many people think there is no one happier than I; they are wrong, I am miserable because I make myself thus.

I ought to have been born a century ago, my most cherished ideals are ridiculous today. I fear ridicule more than death itself, my loves and hatreds are extreme. I do not know which is the stronger, my love or my hate. I am a mixture of passions, which are terrible and strong. I fight against them but ever lose the battle.

My life will finish miserable in a turmoil of passions, of virtues and follies.

You will say that I am romantic and silly, but you are good and will forgive a poor girl who has lost all those who loved her and is now looked upon with indifference by everyone, even by her mother, sister and also by the man she loves the most, the person for whom she would gladly have begged alms, and for whom she would have even consented to her own dishonour.

You know who this man is, do not say that I am mad, I beg of you to have pity on me.

You do not know what it is to love and to have your love despised, but God will give me courage, He has never refused aid

18

to those in need and He will give me courage to end my life tranquilly in the depth and sadness of the cloister: so that none will even remember that I existed.

There are people born to be happy and you are such a one; God grant that it may last for ever. My sister is good, she loves you, your union will not long be delayed, then nothing will mar your joy.

If you have children, love them all equally, remember that they are all your children and do not hurt them by showing greater affection for one than another.

Follow my advice and be happy. This is the fond wish of your sister.

EUGÉNIE

Do not try to persuade me, it is useless. I shall end my life far from the world and its affections. With God's help, nothing is impossible, my resolution is taken as my heart is broken.

E.

This letter shows the depth of Eugénie's character although she was only seventeen at the time, but as life went on, circumstances forced her to modify her nature, nevertheless, her true self lay dormant but never extinguished.

The years passed by, Paca having married the Duke of Alba the Comtesse de Montijo now turned her attention to the matter of Eugénie's future.

Slowly the bitter anguish healed and other visions developed around her, Eugénie was so lovely that men were unconsciously swayed by her charm, but curiously they never seemed to persist to the end; perhaps the ambition of the Comtesse repelled them.

So life flowed on sometimes feverishly, sometimes hopelessly, until the image of Louis Napoleon dawned, at first vaguely then in bolder tones until it almost staggered her.

About this time, Eugénie wrote to her sister from Seville:

Seville,
May, 1850.

TO THE DUCHESS OF ALBA,

With what pleasure I received your letter, and how deeply I feel the interest you take in me.

19

Whilst reading your letter I wept, I do not know whether it was from sorrow or for joy.

I certainly do not believe that your affection for me has lessened but believe me we may love each other sincerely but it is not in the same way.

I shall always regret the days when we were in Paris when you would not have fallen asleep if you were annoyed with me – since then how often you have bade me a cold 'good night'.

The personality of Louis Napoleon now filled Eugénie's horizon but she was clever and the *dénouement* came exactly as she intended and thus it was that this letter was born:

Palais de l'Élysée,
15th January, 1853.

MY DEAR AND GOOD SISTER,

I wish to be the first to announce to you my marriage with the Emperor.

He has been so noble, so generous to me, he has shown so much affection that I am still very *émotionée*.

He fought and won, the ministers have agreed and on 15th February, he will announce it to the *Chambre* in the speech from the Throne: the wedding is fixed for 1st March.

He has told me that he would be happy if you assisted at the ceremony but this seems to be impossible in view of the short time before us, but you must not miss coming for the festivities in May.

I cannot tell you, my sister, how deeply I have always loved you. The destiny which tied us so closely during our childhood seems now to separate us: but I hope that you will sometimes come to rejoice in my love, which will ever be the same and as sincere as I believe yours is for me.

If one day fortune is hostile to us, it will be to you that our eyes will turn.

I beg you not to mention this news for the moment so as to avoid all kinds of anonymous letters and bothers of that nature.

A kiss for Carlos and tell Maria that I will keep the pearl necklace for the first Ball at which she assists here.

Your devoted sister,
EUGÉNIE

P.S. – Please be good enough to buy me two fans (scarlet) the most beautiful you can find. If none satisfy you in Madrid, send to Cadiz. Look for one in sandalwood with silver filigree and one with gilt: they must both have long handles and the paintings must be of the finest workmanship.

Don Lucas will reimburse you, tell him from me. I should also like an elegant Moña of the Andalusian women to match the blue gown which the Queen (of Spain) gave to me.

ADIOS TOROS

P.P.S. – I want my Moña as soon as possible. I require it for a fancy dress ball. It must be very light and pretty. I am assured of your taste so know that it will be perfect. Send it in a small box to Cavallos.

I am sending you for your birthday a charming coat from Madame Doucet. I hope it will please you, I am very busy so Adieu. I am enclosing a copy of His Majesty's letter to Mamma.

Palais des Tuileries,
15th January, 1853.

MADAME LA COMTESSE,

For a long time I have loved Mademoiselle, your daughter, and now I wish her to become my wife.

I come then today to ask for her hand, as no other person is capable of creating my happiness or more worthy of wearing a Crown.

I beg your consent and ask you not to publish this project before we have made our arrangement.

Pray receive, Madame la Comtesse, the assurance of my sentiments and of my sincere friendship.

NAPOLEON

It must have been with a certain sense of triumph that Eugénie sealed this letter, as her mind cast back to the brilliant scene – at the Tuileries ball.

'Sire, I shall not remain to be insulted by your Court.'

Yes! Napoleon had understood. And had acted like an Emperor.

Just before the marriage Napoleon, who had showered gifts upon his future wife, led her into the room where she had told him that she wished to say good-bye, and where he had promised her that she should never be insulted again.

Closing the door carefully, he said he had given her much that he hoped she liked, but there was one object more precious than all the rest, which he wished to offer as a last gift before she became his wife.

He brought forth the 'Charlemagne talisman' as it was named. A small reliquary studded with precious stones in which two enormous sapphires encircled two fragments of the true Cross, and then he told her its story.

Harun-al-Raschid had sent it to the Emperor of the West, as he named Charlemagne in A.D. 797; with it he also sent the keys of the Holy Sepulchre. Charlemagne venerated this Holy Relic and wore it suspended on a golden chain around his neck.

When he died in A.D. 814 and was buried at Aix-la-Chapelle, it was left on his breast.

In the twelfth century, as the relic was known to exist, the tomb was opened and the reliquary taken out so that it could be venerated.

In 1804, the authorities of Aix, wishing to obtain the good graces of Napoleon I, presented it to the Empress Josephine, and she wore it the day she was crowned.

She left it in her will to her daughter, Hortense, Queen of Holland, who in turn, left it to her son, Napoleon III.

Eugénie, on receiving it that day, told her future husband, that of all the gifts he had showered upon her, nothing could mean so much as this treasure.

With all her faith aflame, she sent for the great silversmith, Froment-Meurice, and with his help a larger reliquary was devised.

Eugénie realized the sacredness of this treasure and never parted from it.

During her exile at Farnborough, she kept it in the little private chapel where she so often heard Mass.

During the last years of her life, following the advice of her great nephew the present Duke of Alba, she sent it to the Cathedral of Rheims, taking the most elaborate care that not even the

Pope should have the power to alter the destination of the relic.

The Archbishop of Cologne had asked in vain for its return to Aix-la-Chapelle, but she felt no German town was worthy of such a treasure.

Amidst the frenzy of preparation, Eugénie found a moment in which to pour forth the palpitations of her heart in a few lines to her beloved sister.

Palais de l'Élysée,
Fin de Janvier 1853.

CHÈRE SOEUR,

On the eve of ascending one of the greatest thrones of Europe, I cannot refrain from a certain sense of terror.

The responsibility is immense: both Good and Evil will equally be attributed to me.

I have never been ambitious yet my destiny draws me to a height from which the least thing can hurl me down. But I have not risen from a depth so deep as to make me giddy

Two things will, I trust, protect me, my faith in God and my intense desire to assist the poor and those who ever lack work.

If the finger of Providence has raised me so high, it must be to serve as a mediator between those who suffer and He who can save.

So I have accepted this grandeur as a divine mission and at the same time I thank God who has placed at my side a heart so noble and devoted as that of the Emperor.

I have suffered much in my life, my faith in happiness, so nearly destroyed, now lives again. I was so unaccustomed to be loved, my life was a desert, I lived alone and sometimes when weary of loneliness I tried to seek affection, but when someone cared for me, it proved only to be compassion and I emerged alone and tired.

This man has an irresistible will, strong though not stubborn, it is capable of sacrifices great or small.

He would seek a flower in the depth of a winter night, tearing himself from the warmth and enduring cold and wet to fulfil the least whim or caprice of the woman he loves. He would be ready to surrender his crown if he could not wear it with me beside him.

Nothing is too much for him. He stakes his future on one card and that is why he always wins. I remember now that Pepa, when discussing politics one day, said: 'Women are made to knit stockings.' I knew that I was not destined for them and that I had another vocation.

I have a presentiment that I may be of use to my own Country. Although now I am half French, I can never forget the bonds which hold me to the land where my dear Papa lies buried.

Soon I shall be alone, without friends but all destinies have their sad side; for example I, who only lived for liberty, have now enchained myself – never to be alone, never to be free from the etiquette of the Court of which I myself will be the principal victim.

My faith in destiny grows stronger and something rather extra-ordinary has happened which enhanced my belief.

When Josephine married Napoleon I, a scientist brought from America a plant called Pageria; that year it blossomed but in all the long years since, never again has it bloomed. This year it has flowered once more as if to announce a new Napoleonic Era.

With all this my darling sister, I omit to mention that on the 30th January, the marriage ceremony will take place in Notre-Dame with the greatest pomp. The coaches are superb and will be drawn by eight horses. In fact, I will give you all the details when it is over.

All I can tell you now is that my heart beats very fast, when I realize the long distance which we have to drive, but you can be tranquil as there is little probability that anything may happen.

For your peace of mind, I will let you have the news by telegraph as soon as we return to the Tuileries. For me it is a great sorrow that I cannot have you here for the occasion but I count absolutely on your presence in the month of May for the Coronation.

It is State affairs which have caused the marriage to be advanced a whole month.

Adieu my dear and good sister. This is probably the last letter which I shall write to you before the 30th as I am so occupied that I am obliged to take the time from my sleep in which to write.

Adieu, come to see me I beg you.

Your sister who loves you,
EUGÉNIE

3 IMPERIAL CONTRACT

It was the day of the Civil Marriage at the Tuileries, and Eugénie stood before a large mirror in the handsome suite of rooms which Napoleon had prepared for her use in the Palais de l'Élysée.

Around her, kneeling and crawling on the floor were fitters and sewing girls, giving the last touches to the magnificent wedding gown, to be worn at the ceremony of Notre-Dame on the morrow.

On a stool stood the celebrated Couturière Vignal, guiding and commanding in loud tones as she directed this bevy of women.

A sense of lassitude overcame Eugénie. She had been obliged to hasten all her preparations, as Napoleon had decided that the marriage was to be celebrated almost immediately.

It was barely two weeks since the fateful night at the Tuileries when he had, or had *she* proposed?

She felt that she required a few hours that evening to reflect, and so regain her composure before the ceremony at the Tuileries.

So when Vignal and her army had retired, carrying the wedding gown as though it were a sacred relic, Eugénie thanked God, called to her faithful Pepa to prepare her bath, and to see that no one, not even her Mamasita, came near her until it was time to dress for the evening's ceremony.

'If Monsieur Merimée should call?' was the query.

'Oh, he is different, he can always come in.'

As she lay in her perfumed bath, her thoughts travelled back a long way. She saw herself and her sister Paca, as two small girls, playing in their parents' house in the Plaza del Angel in Madrid.

She recalled that there always seemed to be a feeling of wanting to do things, but of being aware that one could not, because of the need for money.

This did not affect them too much as they had many friends; of these, there were only two who counted, *au fond* they were really friends of their mother, but they entered the children's lives; one for a while, the other to remain always faithful to the end.

These two were Monsieur Stendhal and the Comte Prosper de Merimée, both celebrated writers.

It was in 1834 that Merimée introduced Stendhal into the household of Madame de Montijo and it was he who, taking the little girls one on each knee, told them stories of the great Napoleon and of the glory that he brought to France, lighting in their hearts an enthusiasm that never dimmed.

Eugénie ceased dreaming in her bath and slipping on a light warm wrap, went to lie down on the chaise longue at the foot of the bed. Lowering the lamp, she gazed into the fire where the logs were sending showers of glittering sparks up the dark chimney.

Once more, as she relaxed, her thoughts wandered freely.

She was making a marvellous marriage, tomorrow in Notre-Dame, she would become Empress of the French – but, after all, who were the Bonapartes? She was the daughter of a Grandee of Spain, the Conde de Montijo, Duc de Pênaranda; her mother was a descendant of the Kirkpatricks of Closeburn – perhaps it was Napoleon who was making a grand marriage?

Whilst thus she mused, there was a knock at the door and Prosper Merimée walked in.

Once more, this distinguished man of letters, the self-appointed director of her youth, her almost tutor, looked down upon the loveliness of his protégée, the woman he was destined to serve, watch over and protect, until his life's end. As always, he was struck by her extreme beauty, a beauty which lasted through all those long years which lay before her.

He sat down beside the couch, and brought out of his portfolio a large document tied with official red ribbon, and embellished with numerous seals, then, taking her hand almost paternally, he said:

'*Ma petite*, I have come to read out to you *le contrat* which has just been completed, and which you will have to sign tonight.'

Eugénie stretched her lovely rounded arms above her head and firmly said:

'*Non!* I am much too fussed to listen to all that rigmarole now. I trust you and that is enough. One thing I should like to know, are all my titles, ancestral as well as heraldic, properly enumerated?'

Merimée assured her that he had spent hours seeing to this; so, satisfied, she sank back indolently on the cushions, and Merimée left her.

As Eugénie's body rested utterly relaxed, her mind was active; once more many things disturbed her composure but the one which came to exclude all others was – which gown should she definitely decide to wear that evening.

On her bed, Palmyr, the deadly rival of Vignal, had placed two for her choice. Of course, the pink satin inserted with rows of Irish lace was a veritable masterpiece, but perhaps the white satin with its shawl of *point d'Alençon* embroidered with diamonds was younger looking – the latter a great point as, after all, she was twenty-seven, or may be even a little more, her mother might have mixed her birth certificate with that of her younger sister who had died soon after her birth – she was always a clever woman.

Seven o'clock struck! Pepa came in, as usual she was grumbling.

'The senorita must start dressing – I have only one pair of hands and there is much to do. There are already crowds waiting in the streets outside, streams of them are pouring in from every quarter of the city.

'I, with the other maids, have been watching from a window. Those maids are no help, they only ask questions and gossip. I can keep my mouth shut and it's a good thing too!'

Just before eight-thirty in the evening, throngs of people were massed before the Palais de l'Élysée in the rue du Faubourg St. Honoré: they had stood there patiently for hours unmindful of the bitter cold. As the clock chimed the half-hour, an escort of mounted carabineers cantered out through the gates of the courtyard, preceding and following the gala carriage in which sat Eugénie and her mother. Facing them, with their backs to the horses, were the Spanish Ambassador, the Marquis de Valde-gamas and the Duc de Cambacérès.

In the dim light from the street lamps, the mob only caught a fleeting glimpse of the radiant beauty and happiness of their future Empress, and as if that happiness had lighted upon them too, they applauded wildly, and cried out with almost childlike enthusiasm, blessings and good wishes.

On the steps of the Pavillon de Flore, waited the Grand Chambellan and his officers.

As Mlle de Montijo alighted from the State coach, they moved forward to greet her, slowly a procession formed, mounted the steps and traversed several galleries until they reached the Salle where Prince Jerome, hating the duty, waited with his sister, Princesse Mathilde.

Once again, there were presentations, then the cortège, headed by State Officers of high rank, passed on to the Throne Room where the Emperor stood.

Standing in front of the Throne, Napoleon watched the arrival of the slowly pacing pageant, and his eyes travelled over their heads to that figure in white, who moved last of all.

His heart almost stopped; the vision was to him so overwhelming. His uncle, King Jerome, remarked the sudden pallor of his cheeks, and feared for a moment that his nephew might collapse.

However, he quickly recovered himself, and stepped down from the dais to receive Eugénie. She was very composed. Napoleon took her hand, together they ascended the steps, and seated themselves on the thrones: Princesse Mathilde passed to her place on the left of the dais, with the Comtesse de Montijo slightly behind her.

The Master of Ceremonies standing at the foot of the Throne, cried 'L'Empereur'. All rose, a few seconds passed as officials placed in position a small gilt table upon which lay the register of the Imperial Family – its last entry, the birth of the King of Rome (son of Napoleon I), 20th March, 1811.

Moving forward, the Secretary of State cried in a loud voice:

'Your Imperial Majesty! Sire! does your Majesty declare himself ready to take in marriage Mlle Eugénie de Montijo, Comtesse de Teba, here present?'

Napoleon still under the stress of emotion, replied in an almost inaudible voice, 'Yes.'

Turning towards the bride, he continued:

'Mlle Eugénie de Montijo, Comtesse de Teba, do you declare yourself ready to take in marriage His Majesty, the Emperor Napoleon, here present?'

Eugénie's 'Yes' was uttered firmly and almost eagerly.

Then followed the solemn words of the Civil Marriage.

'In the name of the Emperor, the Constitution and the Law,

I declare that His Majesty, the Emperor Napoleon III, Emperor of the French by the Grace of God and the Will of the Nation, and Her Excellency Eugénie de Montijo, Comtesse de Teba, are united in marriage.'

The Emperor and Empress affixed their signatures to the register, followed by the Comtesse de Montijo, the members of the Imperial Family, and finally by the Minister of State, Achille Fould.

The ceremony ended, Eugénie, now Empress of the French, drove back to the Palais de l'Élysée with her mother, surrounded by a glittering mounted escort.

The next morning before she began to dress for the religious ceremony in Notre-Dame, Eugénie sat down to write to her beloved sister:

Palais de l'Élysée,
30th January, 1853.

To THE DUCHESS OF ALBA,

Yesterday evening, I was married civilly and in two hours time I shall leave for Notre-Dame.

I am in a great hurry but I do not want you to think that I forget you, even at this moment.

The ceremony was superb, but I nearly fainted before entering the *Grande Salle* where we signed.

I cannot express, my dear sister, all that I suffered during that three quarters of an hour, seated on a throne slightly raised from the dais and facing the crowd of people.

I was paler than the jasmine which I wore on my heart, my gown was the one with lovely flounces resembling yours in pink. I have thought of sending you the gloves that I wore, I kept yours carefully and I suppose that you have still the same almost religious reverence for souvenirs.

When they address me as 'Majesty', I feel as though we were acting a play.

Juan Silva has arrived from Brussels for my marriage. He reminded me of the Charade which we acted at your house when I played the rôle of an Empress. I little knew that one day I should play the part in reality.

Adieu, my dear sister, my last souvenir as a young girl is still for you – I love you.

All yours,
EUGÉNIE

At noon, the golden State Coach, the same in which Napoleon I and Josephine had driven to their coronation, was used to take Napoleon III and Eugénie to their wedding in the same cathedral.

Drawn by eight richly caparisoned horses, each held by grooms in gala liveries, flanked by the Grand Veneur and the Commandant of the Garde National de Paris on horseback, preceded and followed by eight squadrons of *Gardes à Cheval*, they drove through the enormous crowds which thronged the streets of Paris, to the thunder of guns and the pealing of bells.

The troops lining the route had difficulty in keeping the people back; the shouting and waving was tumultuous.

At last, the vast Cathedral of Notre-Dame was reached, and the Sovereigns alighted. Eugénie, her white silk gown entirely covered with priceless lace, her small waist encircled by the band of sapphires given by Napoleon to Marie-Louise, her long graceful train was of *point d'Angleterre*.

The Emperor in the full-dress uniform of a lieutenant-general, white breeches, high varnished top boots, wore the collar of the Golden Fleece, which had belonged to Charles Quint, and the collar of the *Légion d'Honneur* worn by the great Napoleon.

As they moved to the golden thrones which stood under a canopy of velvet edged with ermine, surmounted by a colossal Golden Eagle, facing the High Altar; Cardinals and Prelates in gorgeous vestments advanced to meet them.

The divine music and brilliant pageantry made the ceremony seem like a scene from fairyland.

The stately ritual proceeded with all the majesty of Church and State, moving to its close with fanfares of silver trumpets and the pealing of bells.

When Eugénie entered the Cathedral, she had seemed almost overwhelmed by the solemnity of the occasion, she moved with bowed head, timidly, almost reluctantly, but as she returned down the aisle on the arm of the man who was to reign as Emperor for two decades, what a metamorphosis was seen; she advanced with head erect, stately and majestic, acknowledging the reverences of her subjects – an Empress sure of her sovereignty.

Empress! Who during the long centuries of history has carried this title more gracefully than Eugénie.

Brave and fearless yet wholly feminine: beautiful and loving yet never permitting the slightest breath of slander to smear her fame. Sensitive yet fully able to master her emotions, capable of feeling intense suffering yet too proud to allow others to perceive the humiliations she endured; smiling when tears were almost too near to be hidden, grand but simple, haughty yet kind to the humblest, such was the Empress of France.

What of the monarch whose throne she shared; of him we can only learn from his contemporaries. His passport tells us his age was forty-four, his height, 1 metre 70; his hair and eyebrows chestnut; eyes small, grey in colour. Nose large, mouth small thick lips; heavy dark beard, moustaches fair, chin pointed, face oval, complexion pale.

So much officially, but we also learn that he was then fading from the prime of life; he was short legged but looked well on horseback; he had lived life to the full yet he had a remarkably soft, almost caressing, look in his half-closed eyes when a woman was near, but to men at times he seemed 'impénétrable', at others as a 'sleep walker'.

A foreign visitor to France wrote of him: 'The Emperor recalls to me an opium smoker ... the curtains of his soul are constantly lowered.'

Emile Ollivier is even more succinct: 'The Emperor is one who is tortured by the flesh.'

One month passes and the Empress writes from the Tuileries:

Palais des Tuileries,
22nd February, 1853.

DEAR LITTLE SISTER,

You cannot imagine my joy when I receive a letter from you; but this joy I rarely experience.

I do not know whether I am to attribute this to your laziness or your numerous engagements, but your letters grow rarer and rarer.

For my part, I seize every possible moment in which to write but those are few and far between.

I have forgotten the meaning of *dolce far niente* and the days pass without my finding one moment in which to read or really write.

You cannot imagine my intense longing for you.

The Bull fights will soon be beginning, for me it will be a great privation but it is not possible for me to attend them now.

Still I have great hopes that one day I shall revisit my very dear Spain, it would be very hard for me to renounce this thought for ever, but man proposes and God disposes.

Who knows if my poor ship will always sail the seas peacefully or where she will take refuge on the day of the Tempest, this is why I close my eyes to the future and live but from day to day.

4 CITY OF LIGHT

The court of the last French monarch, Louis Philippe, the citizen King had been dull and heavy. When he was deposed and the Second Republic proclaimed, no glamour was lost. Most people remembered his reign as a period of bourgeois monotony.

With the proclamation of the Second Empire, young and old looked forward with a sense of anticipation; even some of the aristocrats of the Faubourg St. Germain, although they would have died rather than acknowledge it openly, were bored by their attitude of isolation, and secretly considered how far they could reconcile their conscience, to countenance the festivities of the Bonapartist Court.

Meanwhile, Haussmann was rapidly creating a modern city.

The Emperor had made him Préfet de la Seine, and given him *carte blanche*.

Soon the crooked narrow streets disappeared, to give place to wide boulevards, edged with trees.

He spanned the broad Seine with handsome bridges and laid out the Bois de Boulogne and the Bois de Vincennes. By building these strategically planned avenues, the Emperor was attempting to safeguard his Dynasty.

In times past, the citizens had thrown up barricades in the narrow streets of the old Capital; now, the Army could control the mob by using cavalry to sweep aside riotous assemblies.

This new Paris was an enchanting City of broad thoroughfares and fine buildings which became the envy of Europe.

Many delightful medieval and modern buildings were destroyed, amongst the latter was the *theâtre historique* built by Dumas père, where so many of his plays won him renown as the dramatist of the epoch.

Haussmann was not deterred by historic associations, but the results he achieved were impressive.

Gas was installed in lamps placed at the top of tall iron standards; handsome shops and cafés lined the streets; the age of history gave way to the era of Commerce.

For this monumental work, Haussmann was created a Baron, and made Senator of France, but the rebuilding of the city cost its inhabitants two and a half billion francs, an astronomical sum in those days, and a heavy burden for the people, when the annual budget of the Paris Municipal Council did not usually exceed fifty million francs. So, to appease the mob, he was dismissed.

In 1891 he died in comparative poverty.

To return to 1853, although it was difficult to circulate freely, owing to the state of the roads, provincials thronged into the Capital to see the sights.

Peasants in their native costumes, the girls all wearing the especial head-dress of their particular village, led by the Curé in black *soutane* and wide shovel hat, moved about in groups watching the army of workmen who were digging up the cobbles and laying wide smooth pavements.

They craned their necks to look up at the new buildings and thrilled with excitement at the suggestion that they might be fortunate enough to see the Emperor and Empress drive up the Champs-Élysées escorted by a glittering troup of Cuirassiers, their plumes waving and breastplates shining as they swept by.

Meanwhile, there was much to see, the gorgeous Calèches, the gay cavalcade of riders, ladies in tight-fitting habits and wide skirts, veils floating from their tall hats, men in black coats, breeches, high boots and top hats.

The good Curé would take his flock to visit Notre-Dame, then, absolutely worn out but very happy, they would all sit in some small and cheap café to rest, until the time came for the train to take them back to their quiet village.

As darkness fell the workers poured forth from offices and shops in surging streams which soon dispersed, leaving the streets empty save for a passing *fiacre*. Then lights gleamed in the cafés and restaurants along the boulevards, as the richer citizens came to enjoy the evening's entertainments, and the night life of Paris began.

Hundreds sat at small round tables under the striped awnings outside the cafés sipping a *pernod*, absinthe or cups of coffee. Family groups spent the evening chatting excitedly on some topic of the day.

At the chic restaurants, carriages drew up, from which alighted men in immaculate evening dress, opera hat under arm.

As their companion emerged from the dark interior of the equipage, one glimpsed the vision of a lovely little foot peeping from under the hem of a crinoline, as wrapped closely in her gorgeous shawl, against the night air, she tripped across the pavement into the brilliantly lighted building.

Within the vestibule, a group of pages stood ready to take the cloak or wrap of Madame, whilst others assisted Monsieur – then, together, they penetrated into the restaurant, whence came a buzz of conversation and a most delicious aroma.

Usually, the *salle* was lined with mirrors which reflected endless vista of lights and people.

These were the years which gave birth to the era of fashionable restaurant life.

At the outset, it was *bon ton* for the *chic* man about town to take his mistress out to dine, in order to show her off to the world, in all the 'plumage' which he had bestowed upon her; to arouse the envy of his fellow clubmen – sometimes this envy burst its bounds and he was outdone.

The ladies of fashion soon decided that it was quite correct for them to invade this milieu, hitherto the preserve of the *demi-mondaine*. Oftimes, awkward situations arose, when a wife, dining with a party of friends, saw her husband enter with his mistress.

As the theatres closed, the audiences came out on the boulevards, some in search of supper, others to take a stroll. At length the crowds on the pavements dwindled, until only a few were left still smoking and talking round the tables in front of the cafés.

One such group might be composed of men of letters – Dumas *père* and *fils*, the Goncourts or Flaubert, perhaps; there they would sit in the dim light outside the deserted café, one or two waiters hovered in the shadows to take their orders, for the café remained open as long as the customers cared to stay.

So they would talk and argue till the stars dimmed, and the grey dawn showed in the eastern sky.

To them, the alterations in Paris spelt dire disaster. 'Art was dead and the City handed over to the realm of Commerce!' they said.

'In the theatres, the Classic had given place to frivolity – a mere display of jewellery and nakedness.'

Having reached the conclusion that everything was futile except their own genius, they pushed back their chairs, making a creaking on the stone pavement, which sounded almost eerie in the silence of the night and bade each other *à bientôt*.

As their footsteps died away, the yawning waiters wiped the table, removed the glasses and extinguishing the lights, disappeared into the house.

Then, from the shadows, emerged the tattered figures of the *chiffonniers*, scum of the great metropolis who crept forth to scavenge through the heaps of rubbish tipped out on the pavements. In the distance could be heard the rumble of the market carts, trundling down the Champs-Élysées on their way to the *Halles*, the drivers nodding in their seats, and the horses plodding unguided along the road they knew so well.

With the dawn came the bootblacks on their way to the Pont Neuf or perhaps to clip a poodle before taking up their pitch for the day; next the water-carriers with their huge brass-bound casks and metal pails, gay in their green velvet uniforms as they delivered a supply of water to each *appartement*, for those were the days before a piped supply was available to every building.

In a very short time, Paris, now truly *La Ville Lumière* stood in all her glory ready to receive her first visitors, Queen Victoria and her Consort, Prince Albert, who came in August 1855 to visit the first French *Exposition Internationale*.

How beautiful it all seemed, the boulevards, the rue de Rivoli, the bois, the avenues, all enhanced by the brilliant sunshine and the light-hearted gaiety of the French people.

Poverty seemed to fade away, and only splendour reigned.

Foreigners arrived from every quarter of the world, hotels sprang up almost overnight; in the restaurants, chefs vied with one another in creating new and fantastic dishes to astonish the gourmets. The Opera, *les Italiens* and the *Théâtre Français* were besieged nightly – the whole city was full of light, laughter and love.

As the Empress Eugénie drove down the Avenue de l'Impératrice, accompanied by Napoleon, in their open carriage with a glittering escort of cavalry, she must have felt that she was driving into fairyland.

By now, she had surrounded herself with a bevy of friends quite distinct from her official court. She had, as yet, no misgivings as to the fidelity of her husband; all the world seemed at her feet. She took no interest in politics; in fact, there were none to trouble about. Europe was stabilized by the 'balance of power' and that even balance would be maintained. True, war was being waged in the Crimea but the people of France as a whole, were unaffected.

Paris was calm, no one gave a thought to the war, and the approaching visit of Queen Victoria seemed to constitute a solemn recognition of the dynasty. The young Empress, proud of her Spanish lineage, desired that her court should be embellished with notable titles of the *ancienne noblessse* rather than the *parvenu* dukes and duchesses of the Empire who, after all, were men and women of yesterday.

She had hoped that the aristocracy of France might be drawn from the rigid seclusion of their country estates or the proud isolation of the Faubourg St. Germain, and her disappointment was great when important posts were refused by the Duchesse de Lesparre and the Duchesse de Vicence. Eventually, the Duc de Bassano became Grand Chambellan and his wife the first lady-in-waiting; his daughter-in-law the Princesse d'Essling was nominated *Grande Maîtresse de la Cour* whilst the six ladies-in-waiting were Vicomtesse Aquado, Marquise de las Marismas, Comtesse Adrienne de Montebello, Comtesse de Lezay-Marnesia, Baronne de Latour Maubourg, and Baronne de Pierres; nine other ladies became *Dames du Palais*.

The Establishment of the Emperor was even more difficult. Many old friends who had helped him to gain the throne expected rewards, as well as numbers of Bonapartists who had remained faithful to the régime during its years of eclipse.

One of the first persons of whom Eugénie thought when she came to power, was Mérimée, who had followed her through life with his protection and affectionate advice, but she knew how difficult it would be for him to accept any post which would curtail his freedom.

His nervous and sensitive temperament, added to his naturally indolent character, were obstacles in the way of his preferment.

After much discussion, it was decided to make him a Senator; this would involve little work and yet enable him to receive an income of 30,000 francs. When the Emperor informed Eugénie of this decision, she was enchanted; perhaps more so than Merimée who had really expected nothing.

Merimée may be compared to Baron Stockmar, the early monitor of Queen Victoria and Prince Albert; he was however, less obtrusive although ever ready to advise and serve.

A true Parisian, he had inherited all that France at her best could produce; he was the heir of Voltaire, Regnard and Molière. Witty and a brilliant conversationalist, he possessed refinement and sensibility combined with a keen knowledge of the world.

Monsieur Gabriel Hanotaux said of him, 'He approaches the great, but pageantry does not dazzle him. He cajoles women but does not lose his composure, he mixes with the Court and the Assembly but does not lose one atom of his humanity. He laughs but does not humiliate, he stings but does not wound.'

Traveller, courtier, man of the world, Merimée was supreme master of the art of intimate correspondence. He sat at his desk and with an easy gesture and an approach all his own, his pen rushed along at random, dealing with every topic of the hour.

When all the posts and titles had been allotted, the only person who had been omitted was the mother of the Empress. The Comtesse de Montijo never received the honours due to her rank, and shortly after the marriage, realizing the Emperor would not tolerate any interference from her, she returned to Madrid, and but rarely came to Paris, living mostly in Spain near to her elder daughter Paca, Duchess of Alba. The Empress was young, beautiful and born in Spain, that Country of Love *novios* and guitars, where girls of every rank, whilst still in their early teens, considered it a disgrace not to have an admirer. Thus it was that Eugénie who had been brought up in a free atmosphere, and surrounded by admiration from her childhood, felt slightly bored by the rigid etiquette of the Tuileries.

It was exciting to be bowed to and to feel herself miles above everybody else, but when alone in her beautiful suite of rooms she longed to walk out on to the boulevards as she had done in the past. She wished that she could call a cab and visit her great friends, the Labordes and others, but this was quite impossible now that she was an Empress.

She, therefore, decided to gather around her some intimates – but the question was, whom and from where?

Amongst her court were some charming women, but they all received a salary, and that alone constituted a barrier.

She could give them orders, but could not joke or be familiar with them; still the old aristocracy held aloof from the Imperial Court, and the Diplomatic Corps were mostly elderly.

Her great friend in this milieu was Baron Hubner, the Austrian Ambassador. He knew everyone in Paris, so she consulted him as to whom he could suggest as personal friends for her. So Hubner, after consultation with the Empress, instructed the Comtesse Walewska, that at the ball to be given by Baron Haussmann, she should present to the Empress the most charming and lovely women of Society.

It was that night that Eugénie thawed many hearts, and won real friends, amongst whom were the Marquise de Gallifet and the Princesse de Sagan, the daughter of Baron Sellières, the great financier.

A short time later, Madame de Gallifet, was sitting with the Empress discussing a ball which was to take place at the Tuileries, counting the pretty women who would be present. Suddenly, Madame de Gallifet asked the Empress if she would invite a certain lovely young married woman who had just arrived in Paris. Without waiting to hear her name, Eugénie replied that the list was closed.

No more was said, but later that same afternoon, whilst the Empress was driving in an open carriage with one of her ladies-in-waiting, a closed brougham passed slowly, and the most lovely face peeped out, and then shyly drew back. But Eugénie had seen it and quickly turning to her companion, remarked:

'A perfect Greuze. Who can she be?'

'The Comtesse Edmond de Pourtalès, Your Majesty,' was the reply. 'She has only just married.'

'I must have her at my ball tomorrow. See that she has an invitation!'

Later the same evening, relating the incident to Madame de Gallifet, the Empress said:

'I am determined to have her at the ball.'

The Marquise laughed and said:

'But she is the very person whom I asked Your Majesty to invite and you refused.'

The next evening the ball took place. As the crowds gazed at the Tuileries, the building almost seemed to be on fire. Light streamed across the terraces from every window. Gala carriages with coachmen and footmen in gold-laced livery and powdered wigs drove up to the entrance.

Inside the Palace, the guests as they slowly mounted the grand staircase between silver-helmeted *Cent Gardes*, who with drawn swords and flashing breastplates, lined the stairs, were overwhelmed by the sheer splendour of the scene.

The gorgeous liveries of the countless footmen; the ladies in their billowing crinolines of rich brocade or priceless lace, tiny satin shoes peeping from under the folds; the men in brilliant uniforms, or Court dress with knee breeches and decorations; the glitter of tiaras and jewels provided a wonderful *mise en scène*.

The enormous State reception rooms with gilded and painted ceilings, lit by hundreds of wax candles massed in monumental crystal chandeliers, were crowded; there was a discreet hum of conversation and the faint strains of an orchestra were heard in the distance, as the guests made their way to the furthest salon, where the Emperor and Empress waited to receive their homage.

That night, Eugénie looked more beautiful than ever, as she stood there, in a gown of light Indian gauze, sprinkled with diamonds, on her head a small crown of lilies in the heart of which gleamed a priceless jewel, around her shoulders lay a shawl of sheerest gossamer, so transparent as to be almost invisible. She was radiant, sure of her sovereignty and power, above all, conscious of her unsurpassed beauty.

After the guests had made their deep obeisance to the Sovereigns, they lingered in the vicinity of the thrones, watching the brilliant scene, as no dancing could take place until their Majesties had opened the ball. As each newcomer arrived and was presented, the assembly recognized and criticized them freely.

Presently, there appeared a young woman, as yet unknown to

the Tuileries. She seemed almost a phantom, so ethereal and delicate did she appear, as she glided forward to make an almost unbelievably graceful reverence.

She was tall and slight, with a perfectly shaped figure, hair as fair as a summer cornfield, eyes as blue as the Virgin's mantle, pearly teeth which gleamed through red lips – one of the most beautiful women of her time – Mélanie de Pourtalès.

Amidst the crowd, all covered with jewels, she stood out in her youth and freshness.

Few could afford to appear so simply apparelled but Mélanie ever cultivated simplicity, and was a law unto herself.

As the young Comtesse stood before the dais, to be presented by the Marquise de Gallifet, the Empress could not suppress a spontaneous exclamation of admiration and turning to the Emperor, she said:

'*Comme elle est belle!*'

Gradually, the Faubourg St. Germain seemed to become more gloomy, the mansions more stuffy, more dusty, the few dinner parties more insipid.

The aristocracy still clung to their 'legitimist' loyalty, but as the brilliancy of the new Court shone with a greater glamour each day, murmurs of envy could be heard in the dark lifeless drawing-rooms of the *rive gauche*.

So a few of the bolder spirits dared to cross the Seine to be amidst the music, the dancing of the Imperial Court.

It meant the betrayal of all their ancestors had stood for, but nature is fickle, and soon to the dismay of the 'old guard', the Prince Charles de Beauveau, the Duc de Crillon, the Prince de Beauveau-Craon, the Comte de Montalembert consulted one another and determined to take the final step.

Naturally, they were welcomed with joy by Napoleon, and, above all, by Eugénie, who felt that little by little she might gain her aim in surrounding herself with the real nobility of France.

A few months later, this exodus was followed by the Duc de Mouchy and the Prince de Bauffremont; by now, the indignant cries of the *rive gauche* had reached a climax, but even this was surpassed when the Duc de Guiche, joined the other deserters, that was almost too much, the Duc de Guiche, heir to the vast fortune of the Duchesse D'Angoulême, daughter of Louis XVI, and now he was so blinded, so they said, that for the tinsel and glitter he was selling his soul. It caused a tempestuous scandal, the Comte de Chambord, the Orleans Pretender, was deeply hurt, but Eugénie rejoiced, and thus quite quickly the Court of the Second Empire became supreme.

When Eugénie first inhabited the Tuileries, she found the rooms exactly as they had been left by Louis Philippe, tasteless and dull.

The Palace contained many priceless works of art but they were dispersed and frequently hidden from view.

She amused herself by gathering the valuable *objets d'art* and placing them where their presence would enhance the beauty of the room.

The drawing-room occupied by her ladies-in-waiting (two were always on duty) had been unattractive, but the Empress with her love of colour and sunshine had it repainted and refurnished. It was now a lovely setting for those beautifully crinolined women waiting to be summoned by their Imperial Mistress.

Next to this *salon*, the door of which was always left open, was a room entirely decorated in light pink, which again led to the blue drawing-room of the Empress. This room was a perfect museum: the most delicate carving ornamented panels and ceiling. On the walls, Eugénie had collected portraits framed in medallions of the most beautiful women of her Court, each in the National costume of that European country most suited to their type of beauty.

It was a great mark of Eugénie's coquetry that surrounding herself with such ideal features she feared no rival.

She was sure of her own loveliness.

5 'EXPOSITION INTERNATIONALE'

During the spring of 1855, Napoleon had sought an invitation to England, and until his suggestion was accepted, both he and Eugénie were distinctly nervous. At length, Queen Victoria approved the proposed visit, then Eugénie became still more nervous, as it meant, that for the first time she would be received as a Sovereign in a foreign country.

She consulted several people seeking to discover the Queen's taste in dress. When this had been ascertained, Eugénie realized that nothing she had in her wardrobe could be worn at Windsor. She became frantic in her anxiety to achieve a certain 'dowdiness' which in reality, with the best will in the world, she never did.

How brilliantly she succeeded in impressing the Queen is shown in the letters from Her Majesty to her uncle, King Leopold of the Belgians, from which I am permitted to quote.

> Windsor Castle,
> *17th April, 1855.*

DEAREST UNCLE,

Your kindness will I know excuse any description of all that has passed.

The impression is very favourable, there is great fascination in the quiet frank manner of the Emperor, and 'she' is very pleasing, very graceful and very unaffected, but very delicate. She is certainly very pretty and very uncommon looking.

> Buckingham Palace,
> *19th April, 1855.*

DEAREST UNCLE,

I have not a minute to myself, being of course very occupied with our Imperial guests with whom I am most pleased, and who behave really with the greatest tact.

The Investiture went off very well. Today we came from Windsor.

The enthusiasm of the thousands who received him in the City was immense, he is much pleased.

Since the time of my Coronation and with the exception of the opening of the Great Exhibition I don't remember anything like it.

Tonight we go in state to the Opera.

In haste, your devoted niece,
VICTORIA R

Buckingham Palace,
24th April, 1855.

The great visit is past like a brilliant and most successful dream, but I think the effect on the visitors will be a good and lasting one.

They saw in our reception, and in that of the whole nation, nothing 'put on' but a warm hearty welcome to a faithful steady ally.

Now that he was married and anticipating an heir to his throne, it is said that Napoleon tended to become more Imperial than his great ancestor.

Eugénie realized that for an Empress, every gesture and movement counted.

She would stand before a long mirror to practise receiving people of every rank, bending her graceful head as if in acknowledgement of the reverence of the crowds as she drove in her carriage, a deeper and more studied bow for diplomatic guests and the deepest Court curtsey which she would make to the Assembly before mounting the Throne.

Still dissatisfied, she asked the Emperor if Rachel, the celebrated actress might come to the Tuileries to give her lessons in deportment. Napoleon agreed.

The Empress was delighted and greatly enjoyed the lessons, after which Rachel would relate all the anecdotes and choice scandals of the day, and Eugénie, with a few intimate friends whom she had invited to join her, would laugh, not always moderately.

One day, the Emperor passing by the door stopped to listen – the result was that Rachel was banned, and laughter ceased.

Shortly afterwards, Incarnation, one of the close friends of Eugénie's girlhood had married a certain Monsieur Manuel, well known in Paris for his elegance and gallant adventures.

On account of these, the Emperor forbade Madame Manuel to appear at Court. Eugénie entreated in vain, explaining that they had been constant companions for many years.

Eventually Napoleon relented so far as to permit Eugénie to receive her one morning, privately.

When Incarnation entered her boudoir, Eugénie threw herself into her arms, then sobbing bitterly, she drew her friend into her bedroom.

There she opened her heart, speaking very frankly:

'Of course, she had been lucky to have risen to such heights of luxury, outwardly all her wishes were gratified; despite this she felt herself to be trapped in a cage, golden it is true, but firmly barred.'

From time to time, dances were given whilst the Court was at St. Cloud, and the women vied with one another in the splendour of their gowns.

One evening, the Empress appeared in a severely plain dress of white satin, without jewels or trimming.

At once, the word went round, that Eugénie had decided to set an example of economy, so as to reduce the ruinous rate of spending at Court. Husbands rejoiced – but, alas! – at the next dance, the luxurious laces and flounces reappeared, and the men once more sighed.

The nature of the Empress was a strange medley of sentiments, sometimes she was capricious, at others haughty as a spoilt child, later she was overwhelmingly sorry if her attitude had hurt.

It is not astounding, when one remembers the Spanish blood which coursed in her veins, her erratic adolescence, and her beauty, the fact of which had been constantly impressed upon her by her mother. From her earliest youth it had been emphasized that beauty was to be the means, ever to be remembered, which would bring her a great marriage.

All this had tended to make her feel at times, almost unattainable.

One day, when passing through her *appartement* accompanied by Colonel Verly, Colonel of *Cent Gardes*, she happened to notice one of the sentinels, a *Cent Garde*: these men were chosen for their height, good looks and, above all, for their perfect discipline. They always guarded the doors of the Imperial rooms.

This man, rigid as a marble stone, looked blankly before him. A sudden impulse to manifest her power seized the Empress, and she smiled at the immobile figure. There was no response, not a flicker of recognition was apparent on his face. Turning to Verly, she said:

'Believe me, this perfect discipline would take little to destroy – it is only on the surface."

'Will Your Majesty prove it to me,' answered the Colonel.

Instantly she went up to the unfortunate man and with a stern expression, blamed him for some imaginary fault.

The sentinel may have been flustered by the sudden attack, but he showed no sign of hearing the angry words.

The Empress piqued beyond control at her failure in front of the Colonel, came close to the soldier, slapped his face and passed on her way.

The next day, realizing the utter injustice of her behaviour, she sent for the Colonel, and said that she was to desirous make the man forget the scene of yesterday and, therefore, she wished to give him 500 francs; however, she had not reckoned with the pride of her opponent.

Her gift was returned with a respectful message:

'The hand of my Sovereign has passed over my face, and that honour I shall carry all my life, as one of the most precious events in my career.'

One evening at St. Cloud, Eugénie and Napoleon were alone. Suddenly the Emperor said:

'I often think it is sad that you never knew my mother. Would you have cared for her I wonder? She was attractive, and in some ways affectionate, but her life was completely wrecked by marrying my father.'

The Emperor seemed thoughtful and after a few seconds added:

'Perhaps his was also wrecked.'

Eugénie was embroidering a little bib, which would receive the bubbles of her future baby.

He went on:

'You must have heard so many stories concerning my parents.

Alas! some true, some invented. I never blamed them, they were like puppets in my uncle's clutches.'

Still Eugénie listened, afraid to break the confidences.

'She was young and gay, he was stern, moody, and yet with all her *désinvolture* she was clever and helped me with her advice and restraint. Of course, Auguste (Morny) stands as a rebuke. When I first heard of our brotherhood, I was abashed, but gradually it became quite natural. Outwardly, I was Prince President, and he was an adviser, but *au fond* we always knew we were very close.

'His father, Flahaut, took care of him after the Comtesse de Souza, his grandmother died.

'I cannot always trust him, but somehow his advice never errs.'

Taking Eugénie's hand, Napoleon said:

'*Ma petite femme*, I shock you speaking thus, but I feel sure you knew all this and nothing must stand between us!'

The Emperor went on:

'You must not be too hard on me Eugénie, if sometimes you may hear stories about me – remember you are the only woman I have loved and will ever love as something sacred, a love which is placed on a high column that nobody may reach up to touch.

'All the little episodes are simply like when one comes upon a shining stone, one picks it up, looks at it for a few minutes and then throws it with a swing of the arm far, far away until it is lost from sight."

Then he came close to her and gently took the little piece of work from her hand and, putting his arms around her, he went on:

'I know, *ma chérie*, that many men are in love with you, some even unhappy. I pity them, you show no sign of even noticing all this adulation. How small and insignificant I feel compared to you, *ma chère femme*, you who, accustomed as you have been ever since a child, to be looked at and admired in the society of Madrid, and now, in the most brilliant Court of France, are able to pass without showing a faint thrill at all this adoration. You are very courageous.'

At this moment, there was a knock at the door. Tea was brought in, somehow it broke the thread of the conversation. Later, when the servants had retired, as the Emperor sipped his tea, his thoughts seemed to have strayed far away. Presently he kissed the Empress good night and said he had work to do.

The Empress remained alone; she stretched her arm and took up the little bib once more. She mused, she had not suspected that he realized so many men admired her. She had had many *novios* in her young days, but now, she valued her position too highly to allow the slightest breath of flattery to approach her.

After all, one of us must keep the balance, she sighed.

The next day while walking in the lovely grounds of the park at St. Cloud, the Empress confided the scene of the night before to a very close friend, who one day, many years later, when Eugénie's life was being discussed and the question was raised, did she ever have serious admirers, told the story to my mother.

At seven o'clock on an August evening in the year 1855, a salvo of guns announced the arrival of Queen Victoria and her Consort at the Gare de Strasbourg. Dusk had fallen, and the lamps were lit, as the cortège of six open carriages, each drawn by four horses with postillions and outriders, accompanied by a brilliant escort, drove up the Champs-Élysées into the Bois de Boulogne on its way to St. Cloud; although it was almost impossible to distinguish the royal guests, the enormous crowds who had been waiting patiently since dawn, were enthusiastic in their welcome.

It was, however, a few days later, whilst on their way to visit the *Exposition Internationale*, that the royal guests appreciated the full measure of welcome accorded to them by the French Nation.

As they drove through the Arc de Triomphe down the Avenue des Champs-Élysées and turned into the Avenue Montaigne, the crowds were standing ten deep and the houses almost hidden by the display of bunting, flags, flowers and triumphal arches.

It was hot, the sun was beating down on the heads of the people, the *marchands de limonade* were busy, the good bourgeoises were fanning themselves with their handkerchiefs, the men with their straw hats: it was a perspiring mob, but nobody seemed to mind!

As the leading files of the escort of *gardes à cheval* turned the corner to draw up before the Palais des Beaux Arts, the bands struck up the British National Anthem and the open carriage with its outriders and postillions came into sight.

Queen Victoria who wore a dress of Royal Stuart tartan with a white mantle was received and assisted to alight by the Emperor Napoleon; all around were happy smiling faces, the crowds broke the police cordon to cast flowers before her as she walked.

The enthusiasm of the mob rose in pitch as the days of the visit passed, the visitors were entertained at receptions, banquets and military reviews – from the ball in the Hôtel de Ville given by Baron Haussmann to the final fête in the Palais de Versailles.

It was during this visit that Albert Edward, Prince of Wales, then a boy of thirteen, looked down over Paris from the terrace of the Tuileries; he gazed at the spires and pinnacles, traced with his eyes the winding stretches of the Seine, glimpsed the colour and animation of its streets, and guessed dimly perhaps the romance of this beautiful city.

Here, on this terrace, was implanted in the heart of the future Edward VII, that love and admiration for France which was never shaken, and was to make history in the years to come. At that moment, France captured his innermost heart, as later, he was to capture the heart of France.

The Empress was seldom seen with her guests, as the hopes of all were centred upon her at that time. The contrast between the two Sovereigns was striking. Victoria, short and rather stout, wore during her visit, rich and heavy silks or satins, without much consideration for style or line.

Nevertheless as one gazed at that small figure, the greatness of England seemed literally to emanate from her person.

Eugénie, on the other hand, was dictator of fashion to the whole of Europe; she dressed with supreme taste and elegance, alternating her gowns to suit her mood or the occasion. Despite her lovely features and superb figure, like the country she represented, elusive and insecure, she lacked the sovereignty of Queen Victoria.

Still, the visit was undoubtedly a success, the first of a long series paid by royal and imperial guests from every land.

Eugénie returned to St. Cloud from the Tuileries where she had bade farewell to her royal guests, as they entered the carriages to drive in State through Paris to the railway station, escorted by Napoleon, who went with them to Boulogne where a great review of troops took place before the Queen and her family embarked on *Victoria and Albert* to cross the channel.

Weeping gently as she recalled the last farewells, Eugénie mounted the great stairway to her own boudoir. She felt tired, the last ten days had been strenuous. She sat down heavily in an arm-chair, she was certainly getting rather large and she felt awkward in her movements. She hoped that the visit had been a success. At this moment, Pepa, her maid, entered the room, as usual without taking the trouble to knock. She was bringing in on a tray, a glass of Marsala and a few biscuits, following her came a footman carrying an enormous cardboard box. Pepa showed him where to place it, and made him a sign to leave. Lifting the lid, she took out sheets and sheets of tissue paper, flinging them on the carpet; she held up the most wonderful long flimsy baby gowns, petticoats, shawls, some minute bonnets and caps, all made of sheer muslin edged with priceless lace.

Eugénie cried out in admiration and came forward to touch and handle the lovely garments. In anticipation, she visualized her baby son wearing these tiny clothes.

Suddenly, a thought entered her mind – HER SON – the future Emperor of the French – then gradually the recollection of the long conversation she had held with the Queen came back to her mind.

She must look into the future, she must take more thought for the country, not only must she dress well and look pretty, politics must be her aim. Up to now they had held no interest for her, but as she handled this lovely layette, ideas, big ideas, crowded into her mind. She must be an Empress; she must educate herself by gathering around her the greatest intellects of France, by studying the history of Europe; she must learn from the lessons of the past and gradually influence the policy of the Emperor; she must dedicate her life to her son.

Eugénie felt that if she could give France a Prince Imperial, her position would be assured, and the French nation would no longer speak of her as 'the Spaniard'.

Queen Victoria was impressed by the visit; for the first time something had come into her life which she had never experienced before, the atmosphere of France, the *élégance*, the penetrating charm and gallantry of its people. She could not even wait to return to England before writing to her Uncle Leopold; from St. Cloud came the following:

St. Cloud, Paris,
23rd August, 1855.

MY DEAREST UNCLE,

I do not intend to attempt any description for I have no time for anything of the sort.

I am delighted, enchanted, amused and interested, and I think I never saw anything more beautiful and gay than Paris, or more splendid than all the palaces.

Our reception is most gratifying. For us it is enthusiastic and really kind in the highest degree.

Our entrance into Paris was a scene which was quite *feen haft*, and which could hardly be seen anywhere else: was quite overpowering, splendidly decorated, illuminated, immensely crowded and 60,000 troops out from the Gare de Strasbourg to St. Cloud of which 20,000 Gardes Nationales, had come great distances to see me.

The Emperor has done wonders for Paris and for the Bois de Boulogne.

Everything is beautifully *monté* at Court, very quiet and in excellent order.

I must say we are both much struck with the difference between this and the poor King's time (Louis Philippe), when the noise, confusion and bustle were great.

We have been to the *Exposition*, to Versailles, which is most splendid and magnificent, to the Grand Opera where the reception and the way 'God Save the Queen' was sung were most magnificent.

Yesterday we went to the Tuileries, in the evening theatre *ici*, tonight an immense ball at the Hôtel de Ville. They have asked to call a new street which we opened, after ME!

The heat is very great but the weather splendid, and though the sun may be hotter, the air is certainly lighter than ours. I have no headaches.

The *Zouaves* are on guard here and you can't see finer men, the *Cent Gardes* are splendid too.

The Queen continued:

The children are so fond of the Emperor who is so very kind to them. He is very fascinating with that great quiet and gentleness. He has certainly excellent manners, and both he and the dear and very charming Empress (whom Albert likes particularly), do the *honneurs* extremely well, and very gracefully, and are full of every kind attention; how beautiful, how enjoyable is this place.

So with unruffled majesty the Queen and her Consort sail placidly away to happy Osborne.

Less placid – a striking contrast to the extremely 'proper' atmosphere created by the English Queen – Victor Emanuel of Sardinia arrived in the French capital aggressively by train. During his visit to the '55 Exhibition the King's whole personality was so truly boorish and uncultured that people were amused by his behaviour.

He hated Society, the only pleasures for him were hunting, shooting and, above all, the pursuit of any woman.

Paris was kept highly delighted during his stay by the remark which he made in public to a certain very prim *dame d'honneur* of the Empress which was that 'he liked the French women because they were kind, and their underwear a Paradise.'

I was told by one who witnessed the scene that when at the Opera, seated beside the Emperor, Victor Emmanuel gazed fixedly at a very young 'ballerina'. Suddenly he turned to Napoleon and said:

'Sire! How much would that young girl cost?'

The Emperor, without a smile, said:

'I don't know. Ask Bacciochi!'

The King turned round and said to the latter:

'How much would that little girl cost?'

'Five thousand francs for Your Majesty.'

The King pulled a face and said:

'That is very expensive.'

Napoleon interjected: 'Put it down to my account,' and then turned once more to the stage.

52

6 CRADLE TO CRINOLINE

It is the 16th March, 1856, and the news of the wonderful event resounded through the City, and re-echoed from its ancient walls, the very atmosphere still seemed to vibrate with the thunder of the hundred and one guns which had announced to the world, that in the Château des Tuileries, Louis Eugéne Napoleon, Prince Imperial, had been born.

The Emperor was present the whole time, during the labour of the Empress; for fifteen hours he never ceased to sob.

When at length, his son was born, he rushed out and kissed the first five people he met, unmindful of their rank; then, suddenly realizing that it was a rather undignified gesture, he quickly controlled himself, saying:

'I am so happy, but I cannot kiss you all!'

Meanwhile, the Empress who had suffered for twenty-four hours, lay on the bed, completely exhausted. When the Emperor was admitted to the room, she murmured:

'Is it a girl?'

'No,' he replied.

'Is it a boy?'

Fearing that the happy news might be too great a shock, he said:

'No!'

'Then what is it?' gasped the alarmed mother, and her agitation was so great that her son had to be brought to the bedside to calm her.

Three days later, deputations from the *Chambre des Députés*, the *Sénat*, and from every Province of France, arrived at the palace and were taken to the *appartements* of the infant prince, where, one by one with lengthy ceremonial, they filed past the sumptuous cradle wherein slept the newborn heir to the throne of France, all unconscious of so much homage.

Three months later, with almost medieval pomp and ceremony, he was christened in Notre-Dame.

Pope Pius IX and the Queen of Sweden were amongst the Godparents.

The months passed by, and the year 1857 seemed destined to be a blessed period of security and abundance. The Emperor and Empress, sure of their position and of the affection of their people, travelled widely throughout their realm.

In Britanny, Eugénie was able to exercise her piety to the full, making pilgrimages to the shrines at Brest, St. Malo, and St. Servan, whilst Napoleon spent his days inspecting the centres of various industrial undertakings.

The crowds almost knelt before them, so great was their enthusiasm and religious fervour.

In the dusk of the soft Breton evenings, the Imperial pair would assist at some village fête where the inhabitants from all the surrounding districts would assemble, the women in their snow-white head-dresses and picturesque costumes to engage in their national dances to the music of the *biniou*. To the simple country folk, it seemed almost a vision, when their beautiful Empress appeared in their midst in a dress of pale blue tulle shimmering with silver threads.

This year was perhaps the happiest of the reign. Outside France, none wished to attack, within, all seemed content.

The Emperor rejoiced in the life which had come his way, he admired the companion he had chosen and his pride was gratified to see his son, the heir to his throne, growing in grace and strength.

The Empress, ever alert to events around her, realized that such a serene life could not last for long, the population of the country needed continual stimulation.

Perhaps she was wrong. The newspapers made much of her great charity in helping the needy and establishing hospitals for the sick, but she felt that something more was needed, some courageous act, some outstanding deed. Alas! the opportunity came all too soon.

The elections of 1857 for the *Chambre des Deputés* contained just a reminder that Republicanism was not extinct; the implication was so subtle that it passed almost unnoticed.

The new Chamber was almost entirely composed of the

Emperor's nominees, but a small group of five Republicans were returned, mainly from *départements* around the capital.

They seemed insignificant compared to the overwhelming mass of Imperialists, but *les cinq* as they named themselves, were a portent of things to come. One of these was a dark young man in spectacles named Ollivier.

So came the cloud, at first so small as to be scarcely discernible in the sunlit firmament of the Empire, but, nevertheless, a cloud which attracted others and grew, so that in the fullness of time, it obscured the azure sky of Paris. Thus began the downfall of the Second Empire.

On the evening of 4th January, 1858, Pepa was bustling around Eugénie's dressing-room, arranging on a gilt table the jewels to be worn by the Empress that night. Eugénie was standing near a window idly rearranging the flowers in a silver bowl, she seemed *distraite*. The thought persisted in her mind that the people must be kept amused, things were going too smoothly, something must be invented to break the monotonous complaisancy into which they were sinking.

Suddenly Eugénie realized that time was passing and she had to dress for the Opera; after all, there was no hurry, she would consult Merimée, he would help her to startle France.

So she dressed and leisurely came down the grand staircase to join the Emperor.

He was in a gay mood, and even told her how beautiful she looked.

She put all tiresome thoughts away, and decided to really enjoy that night the music and the enthusiasm they would evoke, which they naturally always did whenever they appeared.

They entered the carriage which slowly moved off on its journey. Unfortunately, the morning newspapers had announced that the Emperor and Empress would attend the Opera.

As the carriage passed down the rue le Peletier, a terrific explosion occurred. For some moments, all was hidden by smoke; it cleared – bodies lay strewn around.

Orsini's attempt on their lives had failed, but he had reminded Napoleon that he had once admitted *Carbonaro* sympathies.

When they reached the Imperial box, at the Opera, Eugénie stood beside the Emperor. She looked almost as white as her dress. The audience who had only just heard of the outrage literally went mad in expressing their loyalty, and gratitude that the lives of their Sovereigns had been spared.

It was at that moment Eugénie realized her wish had been granted – the people had been startled.

Eleven days later, Lord Cowley, the British Ambassador was giving a ball at the Embassy, which the Emperor and Empress had consented to attend.

Realizing that the tension of the populace was almost hysterical, and fearing another attempt on the Emperor's life, Lord Cowley begged His Majesty to allow him to postpone the ball indefinitely, but Napoleon and Eugénie would not hear of it.

So the preparations continued, the only concession the Ambassador could obtain was that the Imperial carriage should drive up to the Embassy through the gardens at the back, the main entrance being brilliantly illuminated to deceive the crowd.

The only person in the secret was the Imperial coachman, whose hand was still in bandages due to the wound he had received on the night of the *attentat*.

The Empress looked radiant and showed no sign of the ordeal she had so recently endured; as she waltzed and smiled, all admired her courage.

The Emperor also seemed calm and composed. He wore a blue evening coat with gilt buttons and velvet collar, his only decoration, the blue ribbon of the Garter across his white waistcoat, the star on his left breast and the diamond-studded garter below the knee.

Someone described the Emperor that night as 'the perfect English gentleman'.

The Orsini outrage awakened memories in the Emperor's mind which led indirectly to the war with Austria.

When hostilities began in May of 1859, the Emperor left for the front, leaving Eugénie as Regent; she had not wished it, but the Emperor thought that it would be a good thing for the people to become accustomed to seeing her exercise power, then, in the event of his death, she would find it easy to act as Regent during the minority of the young prince.

Gradually, whilst attending the Council of Ministers, she

became more and more interested, recalling the advice of Queen Victoria, given during that fateful visit three years before, when she had begged Eugénie to interest herself in politics, and thus become a helpmate to her husband.

Eugénie, at the time, had felt no urge to take any part in the Government of the country, but now, as she sat listening to clever men discussing the problems of the day, she became enthralled, almost against her will.

After all, her intimate married life was empty; her husband's attention was now rarely centred upon her, except to show her off. His unfailing infidelities were rapidly assuming the proportions of a scandal; he was ruining his health with these orgies of sex, and perhaps would not live long. So the only one to save the throne was her small son; she would work for his future.

Eugénie was not a doting mother, the Emperor was by far the more tender of the two, but she was gradually gaining a stronger feeling, not for the baby, but for the 'EMPEROR-TO-BE' whom she would have to protect.

It was now quite clear in her mind, that she must work and struggle alone; this she was determined to do.

As the war proceeded, she began to listen with a deeper interest to the debates of the Council, to volunteer suggestions and give her opinion.

Nothing spectacular occurred during this regency except the Armistice; and a few months later Napoleon returned to take up once more the reins of government.

In France, women have always been a great power: consciously and unconsciously they have dominated the scene. At times as mothers or wives, but more often as mistresses.

Never was their strength so subtle, yet so essentially feminine as during the Second Empire.

One must remember that since the reign of Lousi XVI and Marie Antionette, life at Court had been dimmed.

During the time of the Great Napoleon, it is true that his Court was full of splendour but his innumerable campaigns cast a shadow difficult to dispel.

The men had to follow their Emperor from one end of Europe

to the other, thus the dearth of handsome virile youth, deprived the women of their main source of stimulation.

When Napoleon was resting briefly between campaigns, the fêtes were magnificent, but they were only spasmodic; beneath the surface of Court life, moved an undercurrent of fear as to what the morrow might bring. Often it happened, that without a moment's warning, the Emperor and his staff would leave in the middle of the night; only when the morning came would the announcement be permitted: *L'Empereur a quitté Paris*, a new campaign had commenced.

With the return of the Bourbons, the Court of Louis XVIII, of his brother Charles X, and later that of Louis Philippe, the citizen King, were dull, respectable, almost middle class.

Since the days of Louis XIV who, with his bevy of lovely mistresses had held a Court of unsurpassed *élégance*, Paris had been the envy of the western world, as the source and inspiration of fashion.

The epoch of Louis XV when La Pompadour and La Du Barry dominated a Court where men did not disdain to wear silk and lace, ruffles and cravats, or to dance the pavane or minuet, with their partners in vast hooped gowns with all the charm given by powdered hair and a bewitching patch. The whole world thronged to France to see and copy the fashion of the hour.

Even the ill-fated Louis XVI and his beautiful bride drew all eyes to Versailles to copy the *élégance* of panniers or the simplicity of the milkmaids and shepherdesses of *Trianon*.

Then came the Revolution, with all its horror, but again fashion mirrored the politics of the moment.

Danton and Marat raved of Roman Republicanism and the dressmakers evolved modes *à la Calpurnia*.

With the *Directoire* came yet another vogue, but now during the Second Empire, with the Empress Eugénie as *arbiter elegans* of gowns, hats, parasols or jewels, Europe went crazy and flocked to the great dressmakers, Palmore, La Ferrière and Vignal.

Suddenly at this supreme moment, there came to Paris, a young man, obscure and quite unknown; moreover, he came from England, that perfidious land, lacking in all allure and imagination. They said he designed gowns. His name was Worth.

Princesse de Metternich, wife of the Austrian Ambassador, one of the best-dressed women of the time, promptly sent for him, saying that she was tired of the crinoline, and wanted something new but exquisitely beautiful to take its place.

She realized that it would be difficult to oust the present mode, as the Empress knew that it suited her; being tall and slight, the crinoline accentuated the beauty of her bosom and waist.

Worth designed some gowns for the Princesse, which became the fashion of the day; his name was made and he became the greatest *couturier* of the century.

He was tall, good looking and well built. He wore a beard, was always immaculately dressed, and with his beautiful and slender hands, he would stroke materials as though they were almost too precious to be touched.

He installed himself in the rue de la Paix, and it was not long before all Europe flocked to Paris, to have at least one gown made in his *atelier*.

Thus it was that a man stood for the first time at the head of the world of fashion.

In the Paris of the Second Empire, not only was there revolution in music, art, and the world of fashion, progress was equally claimed in the world of science and medicine.

Indeed, the French mentality, ever practical, pursued the latest evolution even into the realm of American dentistry – hence the arrival of another astonishing personality 'le Bel Evans'.

How well I remember Dr. Evans, who was our family dentist. He had a black beard. Many tales of his 'successes' were whispered, perhaps fostered by himself – be that as it may, he was certainly attracted by beauty.

My sister, Fanita, once had toothache, and as she was ill – I can't recall exactly what was the matter with her, but it kept her in bed – word was sent to Dr. Evans and in a short time he drove up to the door in his magnificent carriage.

He brought with him cogs and wheels and cases of instruments with which to stop the aching molar.

It was a profound honour, as he was considered to be the first dentist in Paris and he chose his patients as a King chooses his Ministers; and this deigning to disturb himself created a veritable furore in the household, but the truth was that he was in love with his lovely patient.

Much was made of this visit, the servants were almost in a state of collapse from excitement, the whole family were overcome with awe, Fanita's tooth ceased aching, whether from emotion or from being drilled I don't know.

Dr. Evans had amassed a considerable fortune by arranging and repairing the teeth of half the crowned heads of Europe.

His house in the Avenue de l'Impératrice looked palatial, his stables contained a number of horses reputed to be thoroughbreds. His fees were very high, hence his money, but although he only attended the *élite* of the *grand monde*, he kept one day a week for the *demi-monde*.

My mother, accompanied by all us children, would often pay a visit to the torture chamber of this famous dentist.

We all liked him and in the intervals between pulling out my first teeth, and straightening the scarcely visible new ones, he would offer us delicious Boissier *petit fours*.

It seemed somehow symbolic of the fashionable Second Empire that for the first time in history a dentist had succeeded in achieving an establishment comparable only to a prince. Yet, one wonders at the strange turn of fortune. In time of peril when Eugénie's Empire was crashing, it was to the house of 'le Bel Evans' that the Empress turned for sanctuary.

During the month of March 1860, there was a feeling of discord in the air. It was said that the Emperor, who had no ear for music, was going too far; he ought to think of those who had a sense of tone.

Yet, all Paris was present at the Opera that night when the crazy work of a German named Wagner was to be presented for the first time.

On the programme, in gilt letters, stood the name TANNHAUSER.

Monsieur Berlioz cried with shame that anybody should listen to the sounds of unbelievable discord, amidst which it seemed impossible to catch one true note, from the cataclysm of instruments which seemed to fight each other.

When one had listened to and enjoyed the harmonious melodies of Rossini and Meyerbeer, it seemed sheer sacrilege to sit for hours listening to this clatter of cans and pans.

The Emperor had brought this uncouth creature to Paris, the city of charm and culture. It might be a political move, but really it was asking too much of people's loyalty, to sanction such a barbarous performance.

The Emperor applauded wildly. Madame de Metternich, who had persuaded Napoleon to permit Wagner's work to be performed, went absolutely crazy. She stamped her foot, cried and shouted applause, but even her popularity proved no help.

French culture was outraged, the house hooted, whistled and no words could describe the insults which were showered on the work of the greatest composer of the century.

It was five o'clock on a spring afternoon a few weeks later. The rue de la Paix was seething with excitement.

The Empress, accompanied by the Princesse Pauline de Metternich was condescending to pay a visit to the famous *couturier*, Worth. Since early morning the different *femmes de menage* had been sweeping and dusting the *enfilades* of *salons*.

Worth himself had arrived early to give the last touches to the gowns he had specially created for the occasion.

It was not the first time that he was to face the Empress. He had already been summoned to the Tuileries by Her Majesty, but she had heard so much concerning the *salons* of this magician of fashion, that she had insisted on coming herself.

The *vendeuses* and *essayeuses* were still frantically arranging the dresses that would be shown, when the *concierge* rushed up the stairs, arriving quite out of breath, to say that the carriage bringing the august visitors had already entered the Place Vendôme, and would reach the rue de la Paix in a few seconds.

Worth flew down to be ready to receive the Empress; a crowd had rapidly gathered on seeing the well-known equipage drive up.

Worth, immaculately dressed, bent in humble reverence as the Empress alighted and escorted her across the pavement to the great door.

The Princesse followed – together they mounted the staircase.

The second *salon* had been reserved, and as Her Majesty seated herself, Worth standing beside her, the dresses were shown.

What a genius the man had become. He had gradually simplified the prevailing fashion and that day, for the first time, the Empress beheld gowns – *sans crinolines*.

It was astounding, but it seemed a veritable revelation of beauty, line and elegance.

In the midst of this breathtaking transition, a *vendeuse* whispered to the Princesse that a few friends of the Empress asked permission to enter the *salon*.

The Princesse told Her Majesty, she nodded assent, so through the door came the piquant Marquise de Gallifet, the charming Princesse de Sagan and last, but not least, the Greuze-like Comtesse Edmond de Pourtalès; all laughing and chatting in their enormous crinolines, delightful small bonnets, and graceful shawls.

The Empress was so enchanted with all that she had seen, that she insisted that the gowns should be shown once more.

It was a beautiful scene, the lovely women, lost in excitement, buying recklessly the exquisite gown of their choice.

The *vendeuses*, their hands demurely folded, stood at a respectful distance ready to help, if any model should be chosen.

Dominating the scene, a MAN, the fabulous Worth; the greatest authority on dress of that epoch, and for decades to come.

His word was law, not only to his staff, but with every one of his clients.

When he issued forth from the sanctuary of his own *salon*, to visit the different *ateliers*, everyone from the smallest *ouvrière* to the *première vendeuse* would quake at his least gesture. Every word he uttered was treated as an oracle.

Yet Worth was loved by all – he was courteous, gentle, and in his way *grand seigneur*.

Shortly after this visit it was murmured that the Empress had appeared at the Tuileries without a crinoline, a few days later an order was issued from Compiègne – 'No crinolines are to be worn.'

So Worth, aided by the Princesse de Metternich had performed a miracle that afternoon.

Crinolines were no more.

Quite apart from the political aspirations which were slowly germinating in her mind, Eugénie realized that other things were expected of her. Often she would step out of the Tuileries, heavily veiled, accompanied only by a lady-in-waiting, would call a *fiacre* and visit some poor quarter of Paris. There, quite unrecognized by the inhabitants, she showered alms amongst them.

Very little was known of this side of her life, which is a pity, as much would have been forgiven and her foreign origin forgotten, if the country had realized her great gift of charity.

She was inspired in this work, not only by her religious faith, but by her own overwhelming pity for those who needed help.

About this time, Charles, Comte de Fitz-James, son of the Duc de Fitz-James, arrived in Paris on leave from his naval duties. He was young, barely twenty years of age, tall, good looking and always *très soigné* whether in uniform or civilian clothes; added to this he had inherited the witty *esprit* of his family. Mélanie de Pourtalès, enchantingly lovely, saw him for the first time at the house of the Marquise de Las Marismas. As he was coming towards her, escorted by his friend, Capitaine Duperré, to be introduced, they fell in love at first sight.

It was a love that lasted for some years. No one minded, in France this state of things has ever existed, not as crudely as in other countries, but delicately, never stressed, just occurring as a lovely romance.

Whatever took place behind the bedroom curtains, was never openly discussed; to the outside world all was well, all was gallantry and respect.

Mélanie was divinely lovely, and Charles divinely witty.

They formed a Society called *Les Loutons et les Loutonnes* – an association of laughter, where no pessimism was admitted, where youth and wit vied with one another in gaicty, melancholy was banished and amusement became an indisputable obligation.

Its life was brief, like that of similar impossible schemes, but it showed the spirit of the time – a mixture of frivolity, sex and charity.

At this time, even the Press itself seemed to have banished from its pages, any echo which might disturb the serenity of the atmosphere, only pleasant rumours were permitted to circulate.

It is true that from time to time, a pistol shot sounded a discordant note, acting as an unwelcome reminder that some unfortunate, facing moral or financial ruin, had escaped.

A famous writer of the period expressed the universal attitude:
'Why worry, tomorrow another will have taken his place.'

One night, whilst descending the Grand Staircase of the Tuileries after a State Ball, Alfred de Musset, the poet, remarked almost prophetically:

'All this is beautiful, but I would not give two sous for the last act.'

To appease the craving for novelty, the Duc de Morny initiated the idea of a masked ball: for a time such fêtes became the rage. Monsieur Fould, Rouher, Comtesse Walewska and Comtesse Le Hon, wife of the Belgian Ambassador, vied with each other in the splendour of their entertainments.

Now and then, some *farceur* would cause grave consternation. For instance, one night the Marquis de Gallifet, the *enfant terrible* of the Court, appeared garbed as an apothecary of the seventeenth century, with an enema hanging round his neck.

On another occasion, he appeared as the owner of a peep show, carrying on his back a huge box with a peep-hole in the side.

The guests crowded round begging for a view. It must have been a startling sight, as the men laughed madly, and the ladies, deeply shocked, ran away exclaiming, Oh! Oh! Oh! – but their cries only encouraged others to seek a glimpse.

These were exceptions, and Gallifet was somewhat privileged; as a rule, the Empress would tolerate no foolishness, which might detract from the formal etiquette of the Court.

Charles de Fitz-James, recalling the many lovely women who adorned the Court of the Empress, always declared that none attained the absolute perfection of Contessa Nicchia de Castiglione. It has been said that perfect beauty does not exist, but he contended that there was one exception which none could deny – La Castiglione.

Her mother died whilst she was still a child, her father, Marquis Oldoini, soon consoled himself elsewhere, sending the infant to her maternal grandfather, the celebrated *juris consult* Lamporecchi, who made much of her, surrounding her with every luxury.

When barely sixteen years of age, she was married to a charming young Italian nobleman, who was devoted to her and gave her all the wonders of life, until his fortune could no longer stand the strain.

She never cared for him; indeed, she told him so when he proposed, but he was so infatuated that he declared that it would be enough for him to possess the most beautiful woman in the world.

Her marriage lasted but a short time. She needed a man of strong will who could deal with her whims and fancies.

The Conté failed in this respect, as he was bewitched by her beauty, and could refuse her nothing.

When he was on the verge of ruin, she left him.

Her cousin, the Comte de Cavour, that wily Minister of Victor Emmanuel, saw in her the ideal instrument he needed to entice Napoleon III to champion the cause of a United Italy; without much difficulty, he persuaded her to undertake the mission.

A few weeks later she appeared in Paris, amply supplied with funds. Comtesse Walewska, herself a Florentine by birth, presented her to Society. Immediately all Paris fell captive to her astonishing beauty.

She seemed to have almost magnetic power – directly she entered the room, she became the centre to which all men converged.

When, during a visit to England, she appeared at the Opera, people stood on their chairs to watch her pass.

She allowed herself great latitude in dress: one night she would astonish Society by the sheer magnificence of her gown and jewels, the next evening she would appear in an *ensemble* of the greatest simplicity. Always she looked superb, and was acclaimed as *hors concours*.

Under the mask of frivolity she worked day and night to advance Cavour's schemes.

Napoleon was enslaved by her charms, and she skilfully led him along the road which culminated in the war with Austria.

Prince Jerome Bonaparte was also her lover for years, until even his fortune began to feel the strain. She had a son, but lost him in his early boyhood.

Eugénie mistrusted her, sensing her rivalry in beauty and fashion; so she was never invited to any intimate functions at Court.

After her marriage to Castiglione, she posed as a prude, although her inner life was anything but prudish.

She made it a rule to ignore indiscretions, or *risqué* anecdotes: sometimes even, a mood would take her, and she would disdain to speak to any man.

One day, later in life, when she was beginning to lose much of her beauty, she was crossing a drawing-room, when Comte de Lagrené drew near and spoke a few words to her. She looked at him with contempt and remained silent.

He persisted, a group of people gathered round them.

The Comtesse brushed him aside, and in doing so struck him with her fan. Lagrené, without seeming to notice the affront, cried in loud tones:

'Make way gentlemen for the passing beauty.'

'Insolent!' hissed the Contessa.

'You have spoken,' answered Lagrené, 'I ask nothing more.'

During the last years of a life devoted almost entirely to the cult of beauty, she suffered agonies of mind, knowing that her supreme *raison d'être* had forsaken her.

So she shut herself away from the world, and would allow no one to see her, although she had several *appartements* in Paris, she chose to live alone in one room over Voisins, the restaurant, in the rue de Cambon, where she died.

The licence of the nineteenth century, although ever shrouded in discreet *élégance*, was nevertheless shameless and often cruel.

To many women, the marital pillow of conjugal life seemed empty and boring, unless it was creased occasionally by the head of a lover.

The husband, often well aware of this, did not protest, being too busy amusing himself elsewhere.

Well-known names were mentioned, and freely discussed on the boulevards.

It was far different with the upper *bourgeoisie*, and the world of finance. The women of this class could not afford openly to 'throw their bonnets over the windmill', but one notable adventure did occur, which caused a sensation at the time.

One of these more careful ladies, was surprised by her husband, having supper in an equivocal position, in company with a certain royal personage. She extricated herself rather cleverly, disguised as a kitchen boy. Her royal partner in the escapade, did not relish being compromised publicly, and feared that news of the incident might travel as far as the 'banks of the Thames'.

Luckily the Prince of Orange was spending the evening at the same place; to oblige his friend he shouldered the blame of the whole affair, but ruefully regretted that he only assumed the title rôle, whilst his friend enjoyed all the good fortune.

Paris laughed, as the story of the adventure went round the clubs like wildfire.

I was told that at this time, one of the most spectacular men was the Comte de Nieuwekerke. Of course, everyone knew his romantic liaison with the Princesse Mathilde. It lasted so long, that in the eyes of the world, it was almost respectable.

Unfortunately, they kept a dog, which one day left absolutely no doubt of what was taking place.

The Princesse was giving tea to some strait-laced, gossiping women, when the miniature greyhound came in and leaped on to her mistress. The Princesse sternly pushed it away saying:

'Go away, you naughty dog. You know you are in disgrace.'

The ladies keenly interested asked the reason why.

'Just imagine, last night she insisted on climbing on to my bed, and prevented me from sleeping.'

At this moment, Nieuwekerke was announced by the butler. Looking handsomer than ever, he ceremoniously kissed the Princesse's hand, and asked after her health. She murmured how pleased she was to see him after so long, whereupon the little dog came towards him. He pushed it away, and quite forgetting himself, said:

'No, no, go away, you know I never slept a wink last night. You would persist in jumping on the bed.'

Tableau.

The Duc de Morny was giving a ball. It was his custom as well as his pleasure, to dazzle his guests by the splendour of his entertainments.

That night, he seemed to have surpassed everything that he had offered to his friends heretofore. In reality, I wonder how many real friends he possessed? The atmosphere vibrated with the richness and beauty created by the host.

A few people wondered in whose honour all this was displayed, nearly always there was a special guest of the evening.

When the dancing was at its height, some kind person whispered that Madame de X had disappeared. All knew that of late she had seemed to be the 'chosen one'. Where could she be?

Some minutes later, the Ducal host was also missing – a few noticed this, but soon all was forgotten in the whirl of the waltz.

Unfortunately, the music ceased for a while, the dancers were regaining their seats, leaving the middle of the ballroom empty.

Suddenly, the lady reappeared with a satisfied smile, quite unconscious, that amongst her frills and laces, hung the collar of the *Légion d'Honneur*, which the Duc had worn around his neck.

A little later, the Duc made his appearance dignified and quite unruffled, but minus the collar of the *Légion d'Honneur*.

It was such an equivocal situation that for a few moments the guests simply stared, then smiles of ridicule, and perhaps of envy, were to be seen, suppressed whispers and giggles stirred the air.

Then one charitable woman rose from her chair, and going up to the Mary Magdalene of the fête, whispered in her ear the evidence of her sin.

The story was repeated with added details throughout the capital and the theme was of how easily and charmingly Madame de X had won the *Légion d'Honneur*.

7 'PEARLS' OF PRICE

During the epoch of the Second Empire, Paris tended to become a city in which sensuality, luxury and snobbery reigned supreme.

The women of the *demi-monde* for a while outshone, and even usurped the position of the ladies of Society; at no time in the history of the world had such prominence been accorded to these priestesses of sin.

The climax was reached in 1860; then, as the years passed and the Empire tottered to its fall, the leaders of the *demi-monde* slipped into the shadows, many dying in miserable garrets or the public wards of the Hôtel Dieu.

Those who took their place were more reckless, more determined to extract the last franc from their *amants*, even if they ruined the unfortunate man caught in their toils.

The romantic aura which surrounded *La dame aux Camélias* gave place to the studied avarice of Cora Pearl, La Païva or Deslion. To such as these, the end of their erstwhile lovers meant nothing, even if it culminated in bankruptcy, loss of prestige or a suicide's grave. As rivals they were forced to maintain the crazy pace, to outvie each other in the luxury of their equipages, the size of their stables, the startling magnificence of their clothes, or the price and number of their jewels.

Caught up in this maddening race for prestige, and notoriety their lovers staked their fortunes to adorn and keep these *cocottes*; as one man dropped out, another rushed to take his place.

It often happened that although knowing every little detail of their mistresses' way of life, her fickleness and inconstancy, they were so infatuated that, as a last resource, they even asked them to become their wives, to bear famous and honoured names.

It is interesting to recall that many of these notorious women came from the very dregs of human society, scarcely knowing a fork from a spoon, yet, extraordinary as it may seem to us now, in a short time they were so able to adapt themselves as to become *maîtresse de maison*; able to converse on serious subjects, the dialect of their early life giving place to the most perfect pronunciation and exquisite idiom; knowing how to hold their own amongst men of real culture, able to keep them amused in every sense of the word. It must have been hard work, as the men with whom they had to deal were intellectual, blasé and easily satiated.

Only by almost daily invention of some new form of vice, and by never displaying the least sign of disgust or fatigue, could they hold and satisfy their innumerable *amants*, who otherwise would have drifted away to savour some new sensation.

Who were these women of vice and dalliance, and whence did they emerge?

To answer such questions, we must delve into the past and seek their origins.

Far to the east of Europe, on the Austro-Polish frontier of 1836, there lay a small town, mostly inhabited by Jews. I know the scene so well, having visited it myself.

Long before one's carriage reached the outskirts, one became aware of a sour-sweet aroma which intensified until, when one drove through the streets, it almost overpowered the senses.

Here, amidst the squalid houses, lived a certain family.

The father, his *kaftan* shiny and stained with age, his ample black beard covering his chest, two greasy curls hanging each side of his face, earned a precarious livelihood peddling cheap wares around the neighbourhood, thus collecting a few *kopecks*.

He spent his scanty leisure standing at the street corner, arguing with his cronies, gesticulating with upturned hands, and pushing his hooked nose almost into his neighbour's face, as he wrangled on the eternal subject of money.

His wife spent her time, sitting on the doorstep of the building, in which they occupied the basement; in her dirty black shawl, her head shaven and covered with a wig made of silk threads, which had lost its colour and many of its threads.

For her, there was little else to do but to sit on the step of that evil-smelling dwelling, gossiping with its innumerable inhabitants as they swarmed in and out.

If her husband earned a few *kopecks* she would sally forth to buy some offal, with which to feed the children. Hers was a numerous brood, the boys smelly and unkempt, dressed like their father in *kaftan*, round hat and side curls. Amongst the girls, there was one who knew that she was beautiful and was determined to use her beauty to get something more out of life, than a morsel of sausage or a crust of black bread.

In her quest for freedom, she roamed far beyond the town. One day, she met a tailor, a man of small means but whom she felt would be able to feed her, and to her half-starved body that meant everything.

François Hyacinthe Villiong was of French origin; one wonders how he came to be in such a place, but there he was, and she married him. A brief year later, she deserted husband and newly born child.

Her beauty had developed; determined to profit by it, she fled. She thirsted for fame and wealth, Paris was the Mecca of her dreams, but it was a far cry from the Polish frontier to France.

Later in life, she would declare that 'with energy and determination a woman can overcome any crisis, and eventually acquire her heart's desire'. She must have needed a good deal of energy to achieve her dream – Paris.

On her arrival there, the Composer Herz took her up and for some unknown reason passed her off as his wife. Thus she became acquainted with, and was accepted by many celebrities. One day, Herz found ruin facing him, so without more ado, he bade farewell to his *soi-disant* wife, and sailed for America.

The girl found herself absolutely stranded, and without means. She became ill and was taken to a hospital.

Slowly recovering, she almost despaired of the future.

Fortunately, Camille, one of the great dressmakers of the time, heard of her beauty, and decided to use her as an advertisement.

Camille created for her the most sumptuous attire, gave her a large sum of money and sent her out into the world saying, 'I have helped you – now go and work for me.'

Thérèse Herz, she still used that name, appeared wherever men of fashion were to be found.

She drifted as far as London, where she made a spectacular appearance in a box at the Opera; that very night, a certain British nobleman was captivated by her charms, and her career began. She was notorious for the manner in which she discarded one lover for another. Then a most unexpected event came to

71

pass; a handsome young Portuguese nobleman begged her to marry him.

He was the Marquis Arango de Païva and he was reputed to be a millionaire. A few nights after the nuptials, he went away; it is said that he did not realize her true life until after the ceremony.

Thérèse, Marquise de Païva, now had a large marriage settlement, so she became more luxurious in her mode of life. She had a magnificent mansion in the Place St. George, and chose her lovers carefully.

Meanwhile, after a wild bout of gambling and speculation, the Marquis committed suicide.

Thérèse continued her gay life, but to keep up the style suitable to her title, money was required, so she looked around for another dupe.

One evening, she met a young German, who owned vast estates in Silesia; he was younger than Thérèse, but fell madly in love with her. She, thinking him easy prey, toyed with him. He showered gifts upon her, but still she refused to acquiesce to his desire. Finally he left for Germany.

Thérèse realizing she was in danger of losing him, followed. When they met, all his ardour returned. She played her cards so skilfully, that in a short time she became Comtesse Henckel von Donnersmark, and later Princesse.

The happy pair returned to Paris, and she began to build the beautiful mansion in the Champs-Élysées.

The most famous architects, artists and decorators were employed; the result was stupendous.

Her bedroom can still be seen, so can her famous bathroom, with its solid silver bath.

Her hotel is now the Travellers' Club. In this house she entertained all the chic men of Paris, and women of her own type. No Society lady would visit her although doubtless most of them were dying to do so.

She became famous for her *salon*, where men of fashion and intellect met to discuss the topics of the hour; indeed, her *salon* and that of the Princesse Mathilde were the two most famous in Paris.

After the war of 1870, she was asked by the Government to

leave the City, as so many plots and counter-plots were hatched in her reception rooms.

She left for her husband's castle in Silesia; the municipality feared lest in revenge for her expulsion, she might order her fabulous mansion to be dismantled, but she died before she could decide this. What a strange life, from the squalor of a Jewish Ghetto to a palatial Schloss!

The other day, I was told another anecdote of Comte Donnersmark and La Païva.

When first he met her he was not particularly rich, this deterred Païva from accepting him in marriage. He was frantically in love, so one day he told her that 10,000 francs was all he had in the world, but that unless she promised to marry him he would burn the money.

A fire was alight in the grate; dramatically, he took the 10,000 franc notes and began burning them one after another.

At last, she realized that such love was stupendous, and she agreed to the marriage.

The 10,000 notes were all forgeries, but this she never knew.

Later, zinc was discovered on their property in Silesia, and they became fabulously wealthy.

A poignant scene was told me by a man who was almost an eye-witness. It was the end of the life of one whose least whim had cost thousands of francs to satisfy, whose name had stood before the public as famous and infamous.

'In a third floor room at Numéro 8, rue de Bassano, a woman is dying, almost alone, her sole companion her faithful maid, Eugénie La Forêt. Little is left to these two women of the wealth and luxury which had surrounded them.

'As the old woman sits darning the holes in a once elaborate garment, her eyes rest upon the shadowy and ghastly figure which is lying on the sumptuous bed, the one relic of the past. That bed which had held so many secrets! The maid cannot help thinking that if it could only speak, what tales it could tell. She herself, cannot recall all its memories, but what does it matter now. It stands for all that men had asked, and SHE alone had given.

'The figure in the shadows moves restlessly, the maid puts

aside her work and goes towards it. It is almost the last time SHE
will move. In a few minutes there is a slight shiver, an almost
imperceptible sigh and Cora Pearl has passed into the unknown.'

The greatest courtesan of her time was not really pretty, never
lost her English accent, but she had a perfect figure. Arriving in
Paris almost unknown, from Plymouth, in a few months men
were raving about her and striving for her favours.

No house, no jewels, no horses or carriages seemed worthy of
her. The greatest jewellers scoured the world for diamonds,
pearls and precious stones for her choice.

Men paid 10,000 francs for one night by her side; she never
took less and often demanded more. Imperial princes, royal
dukes, nobles and clubmen, she went right through the social
scale.

One night at a dinner party, she entertained a crowd of men.
Suddenly, she rose from her chair and went round the table
whispering to each in turn: finally she reached one who had
never been there before. Laughing loudly, she turned and said:
'This is the only one of you with whom I am still a virgin.'

One cannot leave this theme without referring to one around
whom Dumas wove a web of fragrance and pathos.

La Dame aux Camélias. What romance these words evoke,
days of light and sunshine, hours of love and suffering, then
death.

Long ago, I knew one who had often seen Alphonsine Duplessis, the woman who inspired Verdi to compose *La Traviata* and
who was the heroine of Alexandre Dumas' immortal work.

He told me that *La Dame aux Camélias*, and the Comtesse de
Castiglione, were the two most beautiful women he had known.
Of course, Alphonsine lived some years before La Castiglione,
but the man of whom I am speaking was a great judge of beauty;
he had lived a life where denials do not exist – certainly he had
known enough women for his decision to be final.

But to return to Duplessis. She was about fifteen years of age,
when Nestor Roqueplan, a man of letters, was passing across one
of the bridges over the Seine. He was struck by the extraordinary
beauty of an unkempt, dirty child, in ragged clothing, who was
leaning against the parapet, munching a rotten apple. In sheer

pity, he bought her a bag of *pommes de terre frites* from a near-by stall, but she still gnawed the apple.

One evening a year or so later, he met her again; this time as the lovely mistress of the Duc de Guiche. Then it was that she told him of her childhood.

In her native village of Nonant, her mother had died, and her father became a heavy drinker before she was nine. At an early age she already knew life, as he had forced her to live with an old friend of his.

Finally she came to Paris.

'I was in rags, covered with lice and wore sabots!' she explained laughingly.

This must have been about the time that Roqueplan saw her on the bridge. After this, some old man picked her up and gave her clothes; thus by stages, she moved up the social scale until she became mistress *en titre*.

Her life was one long string of lovers, her house became fashionable, her beauty drove men to drink.

Then Alexandre Dumas *fils* met her; like all the rest he became a toy in her lovely little hands. It was he who coined the poetic title by which she became known. She usually wore a camellia in her lustrous dark hair and carried a few of them in her hands.

She reached the summit of renown in the gay world of Paris; her lovely profile, perfect figure, exquisite taste in dress and her enormous success with men were unsurpassed. Suddenly, a ghastly shadow fell across her path – consumption. She fought bravely to cheat herself and others for a while, but the illness gained strength daily.

She had loved Liszt, but had married Comte Edouard de Perrequin; the latter she left after a short time. Now, feeling death approaching, she devoted herself to prayer, and preparation for the grim visitor who would not be denied.

When too weak to leave her room, passers-by would see her at the open window, her constant companion a large dog.

The circle of her friends grew smaller as the disease gained ground. At the very end only one or two were left; the one who remained faithful to the last was her beloved dog, who never left her side.

In her coffin, she rested on a bed of camellias.

A few years later, Dumas *fils* was seeking a theme for a book. He racked his brains in vain; suddenly Alphonsine in all her ethereal beauty, a white camellia in her hand, appeared before him.

Inspired by the vision, he produced the famous *roman*: *La Dame aux Camélias.*

The Empress suddenly determined, during the year 1860, to pay a visit to Scotland; the month, November, seemed scarcely the time to do so. Various motives were attributed to this sudden whim: grief over the death of her sister Paca, Duchess of Alba; jealousy, or was she seriously ill?

At this moment, Eugénie had many reasons to wish to leave everything for a time. Napoleon was making no secret of his infatuation for Madame de Castiglione; also their intense disagreement concerning the political situation, her loyalty to the Pope and the Emperor's vacillation concerning the Sardinian question.

So the Empress left for the bleak hills of Scotland. She wanted her stay in England to be quite 'incognito'. To be sure of privacy, she did not allow rooms to be engaged at an hotel, so on arrival in London she had to drive to several before she could find rooms. The Emperor was highly amused when he heard of it later; when one thinks of the state of her mind at this moment, one can only pity her.

The one being whom she really loved, her sister Paca, the one in whom she could confide, who gave her courage when at times Eugénie felt hurt and helpless, that sister who had shared her life, was now no more.

The Emperor's health was visibly deteriorating, and she could do nothing. His promises were broken as soon as made; often she had to tolerate the presence of the erstwhile favourite at Court.

Napoleon could not have been quite easy concerning the absence of his wife. He must have realized that the public were wondering exactly what was amiss.

The Duchess of Hamilton telegraphed to the Emperor saying that she hoped that Eugénie would come to Hamilton. Napoleon's answer was strange to say the least:

'The Empress is seriously unwell, especially mentally. She has left for Scotland, I doubt if she can go to Hamilton.'

After a short while in the Highlands, the Empress stayed at Claridge's where Queen Victoria visited her.

In a way, that visit seemed to stabilize Eugénie's mentality, although the Emperor's name never passed her lips at that interview. Was she afraid that if she spoke of Napoleon she might break down?

On her return to France, she became the seemingly unconcerned Eugénie of former days.

Suddenly the news of the death of the Prince Consort was announced: it was a shock to the Emperor and Empress which served to unite them for a while, in sentiment if no more.

One of the most amazing figures of the Empire, was a man who although he played a fantastic rôle, and became Confessor to the Empress, has escaped the vision of many authors, who have written of that epoch.

Monsieur Fréderic Lobiée tells us in his delightful book, *La Vie d'une Impératrice*, that Bernard Bauer was born a Jew, of German extraction: he became a Catholic, then a monk. His fervour was so intense that he passed from village to village throughout Brittany preaching the word of Christ, exhorting and consoling.

Pure mysticism had enthralled the faculties of his mind in a dream of ecstasy, but it required more than this in the years to come to maintain the soul strong enough to keep the flame of faith from becoming extinct.

He arrived from Rome bringing the highest recommendations from the Papal Court.

The Empress had already heard of him, as his brother, a banker, was considered the Rothschild of Madrid.

His reputation had preceded him, his conversion and preaching in Vienna had created such a sensation.

His austerity and holiness impressed the Court, so he was chosen to preach before their Majesties the sermons during the Lent of 1866. Overwhelmed by curiosity, the courtiers thronged to listen, and his words from the pulpit became famous.

The Emperor, although not over-religious, could not refrain from admiring the charm of his discourse, and above all the ceaseless zeal with which he pursued his love of charity for the poor, feeble and afflicted.

The Emperor conceived a plan for public assistance, and proposed to instal Monseigneur Bauer as director.

The Empress had by now chosen him as her Confessor.

Bauer thus became an outstanding figure, run after by the women of Society, as well as those of the Imperial Court. Trusted, admired and consulted by all who counted, this adulation was sufficient to stir an imagination far less inflammable than his.

Eugénie asked his advice, confiding her hopes and fears to him, seeking his aid, to bear her trials.

Beautiful women fluttered around him with hysterical enthusiasm.

Perhaps he tried to keep his head, but gradually the enemy of Paradise insidiously crept towards his end. He lived in a house in the rue St. Florentin, next to the Rothschild mansion, his residence became known as the 'little church' as an almost incessant procession of fashionable women wound its way to seek his benediction.

How could such a state of things end? St. François de Salle, when besieged by endless callers realized the danger and closed his doors, but there was a vast difference between the saintly bishop of Geneva and Bernard Bauer.

Rumours began to spread that Monseigneur Bauer was not always behaving quite discreetly, that he was losing his simplicity and taking a strange attitude, his *soutanes* were becoming too elegant, he was assuming an air of affectation; there was even a fair odour of scent as he passed; gradually he was losing favour.

The Empress grew more aloof, but she never quite withdrew from him as she realized only too well, all that she had confided to him, and that often in moments of anguish he had comforted her, but she could not help blaming him for wanting to assume the rôle of the 'Abbés of the red heels' of the era of Louis XV.

Slowly but relentlessly the human tornado of success entered his soul, and destroyed the religious ardour that once was his.

As the years passed, he seemed to believe that nothing remained for him to learn of religion, or of human nature.

Now as deeply sceptical as once he had been full of faith, the former Imperial *Aumônier* quietly laid aside his priestly habit, renounced his vows and resumed the life of an ordinary man.

Surely at times, a feeling of 'belonging nowhere' must have assailed his soul and destroyed his tranquillity. An answer to this query is revealed in a sentence which he used when a friend of mine, meeting him about this time, asked him:

'What are you doing now?'

Bauer reflected for a moment, then replied:

'I have survived an earthquake, but I cannot find where I used to live.'

Later in life, when elderly, he married a young wife, who was pretty and also clever. Did she remind him of those women who had fluttered around him like brilliant butterflies until they destroyed his soul, or had he perchance forgotten their very existence?

As the buds of coming flowers announced the spring, the Court would wend its way to the fairy-like palace of St. Cloud. It stood between Paris and Versailles.

All that the inventive genius of man could produce were gathered in this lovely spot.

The River Seine ran through its green lawns, fountains played their multi-coloured jets high into the air, to fall in shimmering crystal cascades.

Paris lay at its feet, in an endless panorama.

The interior of the château was a wonder of luxury and art. The Emperor and Empress entertained incessantly; the atmosphere of their Court seemed less rigorous than at Compiègne or Fontainebleau. The Empress never really liked St. Cloud, perhaps because of its mixture of ceremony and simplicity. Biarritz or Compiègne were the houses she really enjoyed. Biarritz for complete *laissez-aller*, Compiègne for ceremony.

It may be that her dislike of St. Cloud dated from that day when the Emperor invited the Comtesse de Montijo and herself to lunch, just a few days after meeting her for the first time. It was on their arrival at St. Cloud to find themselves the only guests, that Eugénie realized the Emperor's aim.

As he offered her his arm *soi-disant* to show her around the park, leaving her mother to follow with Bacciochi, Eugénie drew herself up and said:

'Sire, my mother is here.'

So rather shamefaced, Napoleon understood and had to change partners, whilst Eugénie drew back to take the arm of Bacciochi.

Towards the end of June, when the days seemed warmer and summer was at its height, the hour of roses and shady trees, the Court would leave the banks of the Seine and its light skiffs, for the formal air of Fontainebleau.

Fontainebleau, majestic in its atmosphere of regal splendour, compares well with Windsor Castle.

Windsor, with its massive ramparts and towering keep seems symbolic of England.

Fontainebleau with its gilded grandeur, its innumerable gardens and parks, lies embosomed in immense forests, where gaily clad amazons and huntsmen in tricorne hats, with sounding horns galloped the grassy rides in chase of the stag.

It all seemed to represent an elegant ephemeral picture of France, where all is meant for *agrément* and not a matter of life or death as it is in England.

The whole *mise en scène* here was more ceremonious than either Compiègne or St. Cloud.

The guests would arrive on special trains. At the station, waiting to convey them to the château, stood an array of carriages with postilions and outriders, although the distance was short.

In the circular courtyard of the château, the arrivals were received by the Equerries of the Emperor.

Entering the building, they found themselves facing the grand staircase, then they passed along enormous *galeries* decorated with ornate carving and priceless pictures.

The beauty of Fontainebleau is more sedate than that of Versailles, one is like an old but still beautiful Marquise, who clings to her past glories; the other resembles the dream of a nymph, too beautiful to be true.

The guests were shown their rooms, each with its adjoining drawing-room; their invitation usually extended from eight to fifteen days.

Every comfort awaited the visitors, all was planned, and in a way ceremonious, but one felt more free, as so many people were invited that one seemed lost in the crowd.

The Empress enjoyed the pomp and ceremony of Fontainebleau, and then it was further from Paris and she felt that the

Emperor would for a time have fewer temptations, unless he brought them with him.

She had now become more or less accustomed to his *écarts* but still retained a deep regret that he seemed to consider it necessary always to have an illicit romance.

As July drew to a close, Biarritz with its simplicity of life and freedom from ceremonial seemed to beckon the Empress to its sunny shores, and so Fontainebleau would be left to its solitude, to the owls and bats and the ticking of its countless clocks.

The happiest hours of Eugénie's life were those which she spent at the lovely villa she built at Biarritz. In that remote fishing village, so near to her native land, she was able to relax entirely and be her old joyous carefree self.

In those days, Biarritz was a mere hamlet, unknown to the world of fashion, isolated on the Basque Coast, but near enough to the frontier to give Eugénie the illusion that she was once more breathing the air of Spain. Here too, her Spanish relatives and friends could visit her without causing adverse comment in the French Press.

She walked the cobbled streets, entered the shops and talked with the villagers.

In the mornings, she would ride with the young Prince Imperial as he trotted about the neighbourhood on his pony.

The evenings were spent in the one large drawing-room of her villa, sitting with her ladies at a round table, embroidering by the light from an oil lamp, talking incessantly.

The Emperor would be sipping his coffee conversing with one of his generals, whilst others of the Court read the newspapers.

Sometimes Napoleon would read aloud, but this soon bored Eugénie who liked to hear the sound of her own voice.

The homely life of the Villa Eugénie was a preparation for the grandeur of Compiègne. Hundreds of invitations would go forth to summon the guests to pass periods of eight to fifteen days at the *palais* to take part in the great hunts and shooting parties arranged as pastimes for the autumn days.

At Compiègne in the vicinity of the great forest, Eugénie learnt to appreciate the comparative freedom of country life, with its delightful hunting and shooting parties.

It is true that many of her guests had to be invited for diplomatic reasons; but she was also able to gather round her the cosmopolitan society she loved.

Amongst her most frequent visitors was Prince Richard Metternich, the newly appointed Austrian Ambassador; the son of Prince Clement Metternich, the famous diplomat and Chancellor of the Austro-Hungarian Empire.

Princesse Pauline, the Ambassador's wife, was decidedly not a beauty. She was small and dark, but very chic and intriguingly witty.

Charles de Fitz-James, my brother-in-law, who married my eldest sister Fanita, told me of the intimate tea parties in the exquisite music room, hung with Gobelin tapestries.

Only half a dozen people were present and those by special invitation. Here, reclining on a chaise longue with Merimée sitting near, Eugénie would lead the conversation from topic to topic, discussing medicine with Pasteur, music with Gounod, or the boundless realms of the stars with Le Verrier. Mélanie de Pourtalès, Princesse Metternich, the young Prince de Reuss, Prince Czartoriski or the Duc de Sesto, were frequently to be found at these intimate tea parties.

Occasionally, indeed very occasionally, Napoleon would join the group, he seldom took part in the general discussion, but would sit apart, smoking his eternal cigarettes and later would drive to Paris for his *petits plaisirs*.

To Compiègne also came the Duc de Morny, half brother to the Emperor. Whilst acting as Ambassador in Russia, he had married a young Russian girl who had been a protégée of the Empress, Consort of Nicholas I.

On her marriage, the young bride was given a *dot* from the Imperial 'apanage'.

She was very lovely, with a short but charming figure, dark eyes and golden hair; she was *née* Princesse Sophie Troubetskoie.

On her arrival in Paris, she created quite a sensation.

The Duc, as a wealthy bachelor, no longer in his first youth, had led a life in which morality had not played an important rôle. Just as he was settling down to married life, rumours flew around concerning large sums of money which he had borrowed from a lady friend.

Much of this had been refunded, but, even so, Madame le Hon complained that she was still owed a million francs.

Although the Duc was not particularly friendly to Eugénie, *au fond* she always realized that he was the only one to whom she could turn for sound advice.

From the time of Morny's marriage, the Court took a new impulse of gaiety and brilliance, due to the influence of many of the Russian nobility who had followed the young Duchesse to Paris. Her sister-in-law, Princesse Lise Troubetskoie, Madame Korsakoff, also some enchanting Polish ladies like Comtesse Alfred Potoska, the celebrated beauty Princesse Sanguszko and others. Under the auspices of Princesse Pauline Metternich, *tableaux vivants* and fancy dress balls created delightful evenings.

Princesse Pauline and Comtesse Mélanie de Poutalès became intimate friends, their affection endured till death parted them.

The first time they arrived at Compiègne together, they each brought twenty trunks full of dresses, these were so original and yet so becoming, that the Empress was fascinated.

Monsieur Frédéric Loliée described a day at Compiègne which he found recorded in notes made by Baron von Hubner.

'It was autumn. The Emperor, the Empress, the Princesse Mathilde and a great number of guests, men and women, appeared for *déjeuner* in hunting costumes.

'The meet was fixed for a clearing in the forest about half an hour from the château. The Emperor rode an English thoroughbred, the Empress a white Andalusian horse. She rode dauntlessly, her figure showed to advantage. The excitement of the chase gave colour to her complexion, and she rarely looked more beautiful than when on her Spanish horse.

'She always spoke to it in her native tongue, and they seemed to understand each other at once; there was surely a bond between rider and steed.

'On the return to the château the authorities of the *département* and the high dignitaries would be asked to remain for dinner, altogether about a hundred people.

'The ladies would appear in billowy gowns and covered with jewels, the men in Court uniform.

'When the sumptuous repast was over, "the kill" was sounded in the park. All would go out to witness the scene; it was really beautiful. The torches seemed to light up the forest. The dogs, the richly dressed huntsmen, the horns sounding the *hallali*.'

Amiral Duperré, who was often present on such occasions, told me it was a memorable scene, the soldiers, the huntsmen, the hounds and the poor but noble stag stretched upon the ground; in the background the immense forest, the ladies in their graceful gowns grouped around the Empress – truly a picture worthy of a great painter.

Later a dance would take place in the vast brilliantly lit ball-room. Then the most astounding and unbelievable thing occurred, it almost staggered foreigners who assisted at it for the first time. There was no orchestra, only an old street organ, the handle of which was turned first by Monsieur Rollin, and then when he had changed hands several times and felt completely exhausted, Bacciochi would take his place, and the din would continue without much change of tune.

It was such a violent contrast to all the rest; no wonder a stranger felt bewildered, but the Emperor would just explain that he disliked musicians in the room.

The Court returned to the Tuileries for the winter months, there Eugénie sitting at her writing-table would send for the Princesse d'Essling and the Duchesse de Bassano to consult them on the different fêtes that would take place during the winter.

During the months of January and February, when the lakes of the Bois de Boulogne were frozen, the fashionable world would skate. It was a pretty scene, the sledges gliding to and fro drawn by horses.

Some of these equipages were shaped like swans. Ladies covered in furs, their lovely faces peeping from hoods, large muffs and fur rugs, their coachman on his small box whipping up his galloping steeds.

On the lakes, fêtes would take place by torchlight, orchestras playing and people skating and dancing on the ice.

Large fires kept the air warm. Men and women skated the most intricate figures, the gowns of the women were just short enough to show their fur-lined boots as they waltzed and glided to the music; afterwards driving back by sledge to some well-known restaurant for supper.

The winter of 1865 must have brought sorrow to the Emperor and cast a shadow over the winter festivities. One of the most notable men of that time was dying, the Duc de Morny had ever played a part in politics; he was not always to be admired but he was certainly a figure which would pass down the ladder of history.

In 1865, he was still good looking, with that air of distinction which success and power carry with them.

His lovely little wife graced his home, in a manner which completed the charm and grandeur of their princely establishment. So much depended just then, on the Duc's ability to carry through his scheme, to attract into his net, Monsieur Ollivier, the republican, one of the famous *Cinq*.

With his aid, the Duc hoped to reconstruct the Empire on solid liberal lines.

Ollivier seemed inclined to accept the task, as he was beginning to perceive the folly of extreme radicalism at this moment.

At this critical hour, fate intervened. Suddenly, Auguste de Morny fell seriously ill. To dispel any rumour of this, he forced his wife to attend a ball; meanwhile, realizing that the end of his life was near, he prepared for the 'long journey'.

Charles de Fitz-James told me what a curious mixture this man was, grand, courageous, tender and yet, sometimes, cruel – but withal *grand seigneur*.

He ordered that his papers should be classified, some to be burnt, others to be preserved.

The Comte de Flahaut arrived, by now an old man, but one who had never forgotten that, long ago, a Queen had given her love to him, and so a son had been born.

Now, that son lay dying, the Comte sat by the bedside, occasionally whispering a word of consolation.

One evening a message was received, that the Emperor and Empress were coming to take a last farewell.

The brothers were left alone. What passed between them remains an eternal secret, but as the Emperor turned the handle

86

of the bedroom door and quickly came out, he tried to hide the sobs which were choking him.

So, Auguste, Duc de Morny, passed away. All the riches, the luxury, the *renommée* which had been his, were left behind.

The Madeleine, where the funeral took place, was crowded.

The long procession to Père Lachaise seemed endless, escorted by soldiers and politicians of every creed; friends and enemies alike followed the cortège.

Soon the glitter and pageantry were over, and in that vast cemetery, one, who in life was ever surrounded by the world, now lay ALONE.

So Napoleon III lost one of his most sincere and frank advisers.

Alas! with his death, the immediate realization of his scheme of liberal reforms was ended – when it was revived, it was too late.

9 HOLD BACK THE SUNSET

Paris 1867. The *Exposition Universelle* is opened! The Palais de l'Industrie is streaming with oriflammes and the flags of all nations. The Emperor Napoleon III and his radiant consort, the latter in a silver-grey silk gown covered with a filmy cloak of exquisite lace, on her auburn hair a small toque almost hidden by a priceless aigrette, are receiving the sovereigns of Europe in the Salon de Réception at the Palais des Beaux arts.

The Czar Alexander II, with his son, the Czarevitch, the King of Prussia accompanied by the redoubtable Bismarck, the Crown Prince of Sweden, the King of the Belgians, all have come to honour the rulers of France.

Parisians are thronging the street to gaze at the glittering galaxy of Kings passing from one Gala to another.

Whilst Paris is intoxicated by the splendour of these brilliant fêtes, Maximilian of Mexico is meeting disorder and rebellion.

On the evening of the arrival of the Royal and Imperial guests a magnificent ball is taking place at the Tuileries.

The Empress, unsurpassingly beautiful, stands surrounded by her Court, in a white satin dress, its gauze flounces covered with diamonds, around her neck the celebrated necklace of pearls.

Beside her are her intimate friends, the lovely Princesse de Sagan, the exquisite Marquise de Gallifet, the Greuze-like Comtesse Mélanie de Pourtalès, and last, but not least, the wife of the Austrian Ambassador, Princesse Pauline de Metternich.

A scene worthy of being immortalized by Winterhalter.

As she sits there amidst her Court, and looks around upon the glittering pageantry of the ballroom, the Empress regains, for a while, her confidence which has been badly shaken by the disasters which were overtaking the Mexican Crown.

My brother-in-law, Comte Charles de Fitz-James, when describing these scenes to me, years later, said that the fate of Maximilian cast a heavy shadow over the brilliant weeks, a shadow which the Empress sought to dispel, but inexorably events moved to their tragic fulfilment.

But to come back to that night, as the Empress gazed around at the brilliant scene, she could not but wonder at the long road she had travelled, since her mother had dragged her from fashionable Spa to the latest *plage* in search of a husband, worthy to become the brother-in-law to the Duke of Alba.

Fitz-James told me that as he stood that night near the group which surrounded the Empress, she made a sign to him to approach. As he stooped to kiss her hand, she whispered:

'We have aged a good deal since the first time we met. I miss "him".'

Then, without mentioning any name, she went on:

'Notwithstanding certain difficult moments, I always felt that I could rely on him – now, there is no one.'

Charles knew then that she talked of the Emperor's half brother Auguste, Duc de Morny, and in his mind he recalled the brilliance of that year, 1855, in which he was first presented to her.

The Empress had only lately married and was in all her youthful loveliness.

Auguste de Morny was then President of the Corps Législatif and Charles was just fifteen. Although so young, his mother, the Duchesse de Fitz-James, had taken him to the wonderful party given by the Comte de Morny on 20th March, at the Palais Bourbon.

A throne had been erected in the famous Galerie des Pas Perdus, on every side hung mirrors and precious tapestries, bronze statues created by Cruchôt stood like sentinels along the walls. The courtyards and gardens were almost hidden by rich awnings, and coloured fountains caught the light of innumerable candelabra and crystal chandeliers.

In this enchanted fairy scene walked the Deputés in uniform, blue tunic embroidered in gold, silver buttons engraved with the Imperial Eagle, white waistcoats, white cashmere trousers buckled under their shoes, only waiting for the moment, when after having paid their homage to the Sovereigns, they would be free to flirt with 'Terpsichore'.

How seductive the new Empress appeared to Charles that night, in her gown of rose crêpe with its encircling flounces of *point d'Angleterre* and its trails of narcissus; her lovely hair barely covered by a circlet of flowers with cascades of emeralds.

Not far from the Empress was that other, the Princesse Mathilde; how exquisite her gown, clouds of muslin on a foundation of white taffetas strewn with small golden bees, eleven flounces of tulle edged with marabout encircled the full skirt, caught up at one side by a bouquet of snowdrops – at that time it was the triumph of gowns which evoked 'snow'. Now Charles in mind wandered back to the present evening.

As he stood beside Eugénie's golden throne, he imagined he could read by the expression on her face, the thoughts which fluttered through her mind; even this brilliant scene was clouded by the fear of the future.

Then too, the Empress realized that her youth was fading. She had told Mélanie de Pourtalès that her Spanish maid, Pepa, who always told the unwelcome truth, had said when dressing her: 'You are certainly not as young as you were.'

Eugénie believed that Pepa was right; still that night, as she sat amongst her ladies chosen from the most beautiful in France, she outshone them all, as she accepted the admiration of the courtiers as they bent before her.

The brilliant Albedinsky, Secretary of the Russian Embassy, the adonis of them all Alfred de Grote, later Grand Master of the Russian Court, Count Tolstoy, small, ugly, witty but not very popular, the delightful young Prince Repnine, Peter Troubetskoie, Rouher, Walewski, son of the great Napoleon and his Polish mistress, and many others.

At that moment, the *défilé* was broken, the imposing figure of Alexander II, Autocrat of all the Russians stood before her. As she glided away with him to the strains of a Waldteufel Valse, the brilliant assembly stood back to watch the triumph of Eugénie de Montijo.

Thus it was that Eugénie found herself involved in a series of fêtes, receptions and balls. Every night of this summer was given up to entertainments in honour of one or other of the Sovereigns of Europe who came to visit the *Exposition*. Following their example, tourists came from all over the world to see this new Paris, a city of magnificent buildings, broad avenues and boulevards, all gay with bunting and illuminations.

All this gaiety was on the surface; this ephemeral splendour deceived only the shallow minded. The cracks in the fabric of the Empire were visible even to visitors, who cared to look below the surface.

Bismarck, that Man of Destiny, was not deceived by military parades or fluttering flags; his ruthless mind was already calculating the number of divisions that France could put into the field in time of war.

Perhaps the greatest moment of all that year of brilliant pageantry, was on that June afternoon, when vast crowds stood in the sunshine at Longchamps and the Emperor sat his horse, with the Czar and the King of Prussia on either side, to watch Maréchal Canrobert take the troops by at the salute.

It was the last pageant of the Empire and it passed with a gleam of helmets, and the flicker of sunlight on the bayonets.

The shakos of the Infantry went by, the green chasseurs, the great drum majors, and the little *vivandières* in their bright petticoats, tiny brass-bound wooden barrels of spirits slung on their backs, each and every *piou piou* looked on them as a personal friend; they were truly *la mère du regiment* as they marched, *képi* coquettishly tilted, swaying their skirts to the music of the regimental band.

Then a veritable stream of red and blue as the Zouaves swung past.

Then the cavalry went jingling by, the 'Guides' in green and gold; the Lancers with their pennons fluttering in the breeze; still the Emperor sat motionless in the sunshine between the tall Czar and 'the narrow eyes' of Prussia.

After the review, whilst he was on the tribune standing behind the Emperor, Bismarck stepped close to his own Sovereign, William of Prussia, and murmured in his ear:

'It is all gold lace and tinsel, the guns are rotten!'

The Czar rejected the alliance which had been Napoleon's fondest hope, and began negotiations with Prussia. Then, on the very morning that Eugénie was to distribute the diplomas and medals awarded to the exhibitors, came the awful news of the execution of Maximilian of Mexico by a firing squad, under the orders of General Juarez.

How she retained her composure she never knew; like one in a dream she drove with Napoleon to the *Exposition* and carried out the ceremony with her usual dignity and grace.

That day, the Empress showed the strength of character which lay behind the mask of frivolity. No one guessed the agony of her soul; on her return to the Tuileries still outwardly composed, she reached her own apartments then she collapsed. The shock had been great, the sense of remorse overwhelming. After all, she had used her influence to persuade the Archduke to accept the Mexican throne, now she felt responsible for the dreadful tragedy.

Nothing could change the agony of it all, but Austria must not be antagonized; she felt she must rouse herself to speak to Napoleon.

So a short time later, the Emperor Franz Joseph was approached with the suggestion that the Imperial couple should meet him at Salzburg; to this he agreed.

Franz Joseph was accompanied by his beautiful young wife, Elizabeth, a perfect contrast to Eugénie.

Notwithstanding the difference of age, they became friends. In a way they had much in common; the love of horses, the enjoyment of travelling and both had rather unfaithful husbands.

All this formed a bond of *camaraderie* which lasted until death came to one of them.

It was a strange situation, this meeting of the two Empresses, the one radiant with youth, born of a royal race; the other, no longer young, Consort of one who felt the power slipping from his grasp.

Wisely, Eugénie drew back, giving place of honour to Elizabeth, thus winning her favour; an alliance with Austria might have been negotiated but Napoleon, as always, was hesitant, and Eugénie mistrustful.

So it all came to nothing; France was left without allies on the Continent of Europe.

Italy might have helped, but her price would have been Rome, and Eugénie, always a devout Catholic, would not consider wresting the last shreds of temporal power from the Pope.

In her anxiety, Eugénie longed to turn to Queen Victoria, but she knew that it was almost impossible to approach her, as the Queen was daily growing more antagonistic to Napoleon's policy in regard to the Italian question.

A proof of this had lately occurred when the Prince and Princess of Wales passed through Paris on their return from the Near East; orders came from Windsor that on no account were the young couple to stay at Compiègne; they could go to lunch and that was all, as they must understand that the mode of life of the French Court was unsuitable for young people newly married.

As the year 1867 drew to its close, the Emperor's illness seemed to increase and at times caused him great suffering, but still he continued to lead the life which had been strictly forbidden by his doctors.

The Empress realized the state of her husband's health. She took his place whenever he was physically unfit to fulfil his numerous engagements, she seemed to resent his inability to thrust his suffering aside, and could not help attributing it to his amorous excesses.

Perhaps it was only now that she sensed the unrest, which was working like a canker at the heart of the Empire. The Press was actively hostile; behind the cheering of the crowd she could feel the disaffection.

The Second Empire was nearing its end. The Mexican adventure and the Austrian war had helped to undermine its foundations. All around, the nations were arming. War was drawing near, the people of France lived but for the day; not daring to forecast the future.

Mélanie de Pourtalès warned the Emperor of the Prussian menace on her return from Germany; even Merimée spoke in vain. Napoleon refused to listen, he could not believe that they would ever dare to attack France.

Eugénie was more clear sighted. She saw the dangers both at home and abroad, but was unable to influence Napoleon.

The Prince Imperial reached his twelfth birthday in 1868 amidst great rejoicings, in which all France participated officially. Eugénie as she entered his room that morning, kissed him fondly and poured forth all her loving wishes and blessings. Of late, as she had watched her son, both during his hours of study and as he played with his young companions beneath her windows, she had feared lest the adulation of the public might spoil his nature.

Au fond she realized that she knew so little of her child, his reactions were contrary to her own; he was determined, in a way stubborn, studious and yet light-hearted, at times even frivolous. He had been prepared for his first communion for some months now, and she trusted that he would realize the wonder of it all when the moment came for him to receive his Blessed Lord.

L'Abbé Duguerry had done his best by precept and admonition to instil into his pupil a realization of the sacrifices expected from one of his exalted rank.

Only a few days ago, Eugénie had entered her son's room, to find a letter, or was it a memorandum, in the Abbé's handwriting addressed to the Prince Imperial.

She picked it up and tears came into her eyes as she read:

MON CHER PETIT SEIGNEUR,

As a new born child, you were invested with the Grand Cordon of the Légion d'Honneur; that you know, is one of the most precious rewards of merit. What service could you possibly have rendered to your Country at two days old?

It was given to you, mon cher petit Seigneur, not for services you had rendered, but for those that you would have to render in the years to come.

It was a sign, that even in the cradle, you belonged wholly to France and to the people of France.

The deference paid by men to Royalty, is not a birthright, nor a slavish empty form, it is the continual acknowledgment of a Sacrifice, not required from other people.

Others are free, within the bounds of Christian duty, but a Sovereign has no life or purpose of his own.

When men call him 'Majesty' and remain standing in his presence, it is because they do homage, not to the Power and Glory, but to the Abnegation required of the wearer of a Crown.

Laying the paper on the table she left the room; all her misgivings had fled. She knew that with such an instructor to guide his steps, her son would be safe.

Almost immediately after the ceremony of the First Communion in the Chapel of the Tuileries, the young Prince deputized for his father at Chalons and received the foreign generals who attended the review.

All went off magnificently. He reflected great credit upon his enraptured tutors, they felt that their pupil's glorious career was just beginning; actually it was the last review he ever held.

Everywhere he went in the provinces he was received with frantic ovations.

In 1869, the centenary of his great ancestor, he travelled with the Empress to Corsica; the Emperor being too ill to make the journey.

Eugénie thought to 'walk upon flowers but had to put up with official nosegays'.

As for her son, his very appearance caused scenes of delirious enthusiasm.

When he stood before the birthplace of the Great Napoleon, the crowd burst all bounds, overwhelming his entourage and crushing them against the walls.

The Prince, not a bit dismayed, turned with starry eyes and cried: 'Oh! do let them come in, they are part of my family.'

Surely the young boy had before him the vision of a glorious future; but it was not to be.

Even then, Octave Feuillet wrote: 'Men of goodwill scarcely believe in a tomorrow, in making their plans for the future the Empire is left out.'

Merimée, the most fervid apostle of the epoch, said: 'Everyone is afraid and hardly knows why – it is like Mozart's music before the appearance of the commander.'

Eugénie somewhat disillusioned by her own personal reception in Corsica, was deeply disturbed by the political unrest which manifested itself more and more throughout the land, reaching a climax on the day of a gala performance in Paris in honour of the Queen of Holland.

That evening, as Eugénie was being arrayed in all her glory by Pepa, who as usual was full of gloomy forebodings, the door flew open and the Prince Imperial appeared, rather dishevelled and flushed with excitement.

'Maman,' he cried, 'there is a noisy crowd in the Place du Carrousel. Conneau says they are shouting *à bas Badinguet!* Who is Badinguet, Maman?'

The Empress told Pepa to cease talking and herself went to the window. Drawing the curtains closely, she said to her son:

'*Ce n'est rien:* the people have only come to watch the guests arrive.'

'But why are you trembling, Maman?'

'Don't ask questions, Louis! Go to Monsieur Filon who is waiting to hear your evening prayers.'

It was at this time, when politics both at home and abroad were a matter for grave anxiety that the Khedive of Egypt came to Paris to beg the Empress to declare the Suez Canal open to the shipping of the world.

Eugénie was delighted at the success which had crowned the efforts of her cousin, Ferdinand de Lesseps.

He was a link with the happy days of her carefree girlhood in Sunny Spain; he had been *en poste* at the French Embassy in Madrid.

She had enthusiastically supported his scheme for cutting a ship canal through the Isthmus of Suez, and even persuaded the French Government to purchase a vast number of shares; an act, regarded at the time with grave suspicion, later generations learnt to appreciate her clear-sighted vision in this matter.

It was in the month of October 1869, that the Empress set out on her six weeks' tour. She took with her a brilliant entourage: Prince Joachim Murat, Comte de Cossé-Brissac, Madame de Nadaillac, Madame de la Poëz, her sister Paca's daughters and others.

She left Venice for Constantinople in the Imperial yacht *Aigle*; the Sultan of Turkey received her with Oriental splendour, giving a magnificent entertainment in her honour at the Yildez Kiosk: then she left for Egypt.

In Cairo, she stayed in a palace specially built for her by the Khedive; a few days later she sailed slowly up the Nile in a gaily decorated *dahabiya* followed by a long retinue of vessels. Like a modern Cleopatra she passed in stately procession up the river, visiting ruined temples by moonlight and inspecting the excavations recently opened in the Valley of the Kings. Then she returned to Port Said to receive the Emperor Francis Joseph of Austria and a host of other Royal visitors.

It was an hour of personal triumph, when on 16th November, 1869, her yacht led the splendid procession into the new canal, amidst the cheering of thousands, fanfares of trumpets and the thunder of guns.

It was a triumph for her as Empress, for she realized that it was thanks to her foresight that the canal was a French enterprise, the only foreign shares being those allotted to the Khedive as the price of the concession.

She fondly hoped that this success might serve to draw the attention of the public from the unrest at home and perhaps stave off the disaster she feared.

It was a triumph for Eugénie as a woman; she knew that in the midst of these splendid fêtes, she reigned supreme, a vision of loveliness.

She had taken with her a huge wardrobe of gowns, creations of filmy gauze and sparkling tulle; the result of Worth's almost divine inspiration, and she moved through the marvellous scenes of pageantry, like an ethereal being scarcely of this earth.

In after years, she spoke of these weeks 'as my most splendid memories'.

There, in the soft caressing air of the Egyptian nights, she felt a release from the gloom and anxiety which had enveloped her during the last months. Certainly for this brief space of time, she unfolded like an exotic flower to bloom anew in this courtly atmosphere of more than Oriental splendour.

10   FLIGHT IN THE DAWN

As the bells of Paris rang in the New Year of 1870, war clouds were gathering on the horizon.

The intrigues of Bismarck had successfully isolated France from her potential allies.

The candidature of Prince Leopold of Hohenzollern for the Spanish throne provided the excuse for a rupture. Napoleon demanded a guarantee that his claim should not be supported by Prussia. By skilful diplomacy the onus of a declaration of war was thrust upon France in such a way that national honour could be satisfied with nothing less.

The very newsboys ran wildly through the streets crying, '*À Berlin! À Berlin!*'

Napoleon who had been suffering agonies from his malady was in no condition to deal with the situation.

Eugénie did not fear war, but she dreaded Revolution: this war was undoubtedly popular with the masses, she visualized her husband returning in triumph after a brief campaign.

The young Prince was to go to the front with his father. He was still only a boy of fourteen, but he was so proud of his new uniform as a second lieutenant, that Eugénie hid her anguish and bade him God Speed as they left by train for Metz.

Thus the Empress found herself Regent in the grim hour of France's travail: a brief initial success, then nothing – disorganization, incompetence, disaster.

After the defeat of the army at Forbach and the invasion of Alsace, Eugénie still believing in her power to save the situation, thought only of her son – the Emperor no longer counted – defeated he ceased to exist in her mind.

Now, her only thought was for her child; he must be saved. She told Filon, his tutor, to telegraph to Duperré to take him to Belgium. She prayed that it was not too late.

Then came the news of the Emperor's surrender. Quickly events followed one another. Advisers surrounded her but she would listen to none. Eugénie shut her ears to the cries and curses of the surging mob.

As she stood there defiantly, a deputation from the Corps Législatif was announced and the three ministers, Jerome David, Busson-Billault and Henri Chevreau, entered. They respectfully implored her to listen to the truth. All was lost. The Empress drawing herself up exclaimed: 'Here I am and here I stay.'

At this, the Prince de Conti, Chef du Cabinet, asked to speak to her in private.

'Majesty,' he said solemnly, 'if you go, you do not abdicate; if you stay, in one short hour, you will be in the hands of those who will force you to abdicate.'

Now the mob were rioting in the Place de la Concorde, the National Guard had joined them, order was at an end. She knew that she must go.

Leaving the Tuileries, she entered the Louvre by the Galerie de Diane.

Whilst passing along a corridor, she saw the flag falling from its tall staff on the Pavillon de l'Horloge, to lie a tattered rag on the stones below. Someone had cut it down.

She came to a private door leading to the Place St. Germain l'Auxerrois, the crowds were screaming, 'Death to the Spanish woman', '*Vive la République*'. She stepped out on the pavement; someone summoned a passing *fiacre*; entering it with one companion, her reader Madame Lebreton, she drove to the house of a friend.

Alas, he was away; then they drove to the *appartement* of her Chamberlain in the Avenue Wagram; he too was absent from home. Then Eugénie bethought herself of one last possibility, her American dentist, Dr. Evans.

Later, as she sat in his reception room, awaiting the return of the only friend to whom she could turn in this tragic hour, she must have mused upon the extraordinary situation in which she found herself.

Dr. Evans came in, and was startled to find the Empress there.

He gave her food, and she lay down fully dressed on the bed, whilst he hurried out to make the necessary arrangements for her flight. What lonely desolation must have faced the Empress as she waited in this unused room of the house in the Avenue de l'Impèratrice. It seemed so few years ago that she conquered Paris with the Emperor by her side and now she was about to escape from that city, her only friends her dentist and Madame Lebreton. Her husband a prisoner – her beloved son a fugitive, in an alien country. God protect him and grant that Duperré may bring him safe to England!   ,

Whilst the Empress rested, Dr. Evans and Madame Lebreton sat in arm-chairs in his consulting room waiting the hour of 5 a.m., when they would have to begin the weary trail to the sea coast.

The story of this tragic journey was related some time later to my mother by Dr. Evans, who wrote it down, and here I give the story in her own words:

'I had just come from my consulting room, the whole day had been tiring as patients whom I had begun to treat, had flocked to me, imploring me to finish what I was doing, as the state of affairs in the City had made them anxious.

'Suddenly, my valet came rushing in saying: "There are two ladies asking for you, sir, one is heavily veiled, but I think I recognize the Empress." I hastened to the room, as I entered the Empress stood before me. She looked startled and had a frightened expression in her eyes.

'Although standing quite erect, I recall that she was supporting herself by holding the back of a chair. In her inimitable voice, she said: "Monsieur Evans, I have no friends left but yourself. I come as a fugitive to beg your help."

'At once the thought leapt to my mind that I was giving a dinner party in an hour's time, it was five o'clock and they would arrive precisely at six o'clock. What should I do? Then I said: "Madame, I shall do everything in my power to help Your Majesty."

'To Madame Lebreton who accompanied the Empress, I

whispered of my plight and she spoke to the Empress, who said: "I shall not be in your way. Act to your guests as if you know nothing of my whereabouts." Of course, by then, rumours were spreading that the Empress had left the Tuileries.

'I scarcely realized what was taking place, to have to receive and entertain twenty people and act as the Empress had asked me to, when all the time I knew that she was sitting in a small cold room where I could not for the life of me remember if I had ordered a fire to be lit.

'As only my valet knew that the Empress was under my roof I could not tell the footmen to take her food; it was too dangerous.

'After dinner, on the pretext of fetching special cigars I flew to the little room. The fire had been lit, but the Empress murmured "*J'ai faim*", so I called the valet and told him to go to the larder when the chef was occupied elsewhere and bring on a tray whatever he could find for the two ladies. Armed with the box of cigars I hurried back to my guests. It seemed as though they would never go, and it was midnight before the last took his leave.

'When I went back to the little room, I found the Empress almost in a state of collapse, and Madame Lebreton not much better.

'I rushed to my bedroom to change and prepare for the journey.

'My brown landau had been ordered for 5 a.m.: the Empress sat on the left, Madame Lebreton beside her, Crane and myself on the front seat.

'It was a dreadful journey, my one idea was to reach a port on the coast where we could charter a vessel of some kind. As we passed through villages and towns, there were scenes of excitement and rejoicing as the Republic was proclaimed.'

The bells of the Angelus were ringing as the carriage drove into Deauville. Soon a place of rest and seclusion was found for the Empress and Madame Lebreton.

The former was supposed to be an English lady who was mentally deranged, accompanied by her nurse. Strict orders were given that nobody should be permitted to approach her.

In the meanwhile, Dr. Evans and his nephew sauntered down

to Trouville harbour in search of a means of escape. There he saw an English yacht. What followed is best described in Sir John Burgoyne's own words in a letter which he wrote to Colonel Ponsonby, Private Secretary to Queen Victoria.

Windsor House, Ryde, I.O.W.
15th September, 1870.

MY DEAR PONSONBY,

I am very glad to give you a short account of the extraordinary circumstances of my bringing H.I.M. the Empress over in the *Gazelle.*

I am specially anxious that it should be known, that all that occurred was by the most pure accident, as I fear an impression has got abroad that I was in Deauville Harbour 'waiting events'. Lady Burgoyne had been abroad for some months, and I went in the yacht to Trouville (Deauville Harbour) to meet her on 24th August. We were detained there by bad weather and head winds, longer than we expected and so much did we wish to get away that on two occasions I was ready for sea and had the pilot on board but, by his advice, did not go out. I mention these details to prove I am not mixed up in foreign complications.

On Tuesday the 6th September at about 2 p.m. two strangers came on board and asked to be allowed to see an English yacht. I happened to be on board and myself showed them over the yacht; one of them suddenly asked to be allowed to say a few words in private; he then informed me that the Empress was concealed in Deauville, wishing to be conveyed to England, and asked me if I would undertake to take her over in the yacht.

After consulting with Lady Burgoyne and considering the scanty accommodation on board, I at once agreed to her request, it was considered advisable that Lady Burgoyne should remain on board, as her landing might create suspicion.

It was arranged between the two gentlemen (Dr. Evans and his nephew) and myself that I was to meet them at a certain place on the quay at 11 p.m. that night, to settle at what time Her Majesty was to come aboard.

We met and settled the hour for five minutes past twelve (midnight). Oddly enough at 11.30 p.m. I had the honour of a visit from a young Russian gentleman, to whom I had only been introduced casually, who brought 'a friend of his from Paris, who was anxious to see a yacht.'

I had the pleasure of showing them all over the vessel, except Lady Burgoyne's cabin, and have little doubt that he was a spy, who suspected something.

I carefully watched these two persons back over the railway bridge into Trouville, and while I was doing so, Dr. Evans, the Empress and Madame Lebreton came up and I immediately took them on board.

The Empress was very much agitated and sobbed bitterly and on my saying to her when going on board: '*N'ayez pas peur, Madame,*' she replied in English, 'I am safe with an English gentleman.'

I then introduced her to my wife, who told her the last three days' news and read the papers to her.

At seven o'clock, we left the harbour, and had very heavy weather with a nasty sea running, but the *Gazelle* is a very fine sea boat and behaved splendidly. I fear the Empress must have suffered frightful discomfort, although we did all in our power to make her comfortable.

I landed with the Empress at Ryde a little before seven on the 8th, and she left at midday via Portsmouth for Hastings to rejoin her son.

If her Majesty, the Queen, should speak to you about this occurrence, I shall deem it an immense favour if you will thoroughly explain that my part in it was entirely from accident, and that, previous to 2 p.m. on the 6th, I do not think I ever heard the Empress's name mentioned while I was in France.

The Empress had no luggage of any sort or kind and what she had to undergo in her journey from Paris to Deauville had far better never be known.

Monsieur de Lesseps had nothing whatever to do with her escape. I believe Prince Metternich planned it, and Dr. Evans carried it out most skilfully.

We are plunged into the deepest affliction by the loss of H.M.S. *Captain* (which sank in the Channel that night) and of poor Hugh Burgoyne, who as you know, is not a relative of mine, yet was my dearest friend, his poor wife and mine are inseparable. She is in a very unsatisfactory state; the sudden blow has almost deprived her of reason.

His father, the poor old Field Marshal (Sir John Burgoyne) is completely bowed down by the catastrophe and at his great age (88) it is the more terrible. . . .

Believe me,

Yours very truly,

J. MONTAGU BURGOYNE.

Some time later, recalling that terrible journey, the Empress said that she would never be able sufficiently to thank Sir John and his charming wife for their wonderful courage in risking their lives to aid her escape that night. She felt that it was so typical of an English lady to act as she did; she was gay, full of attention and yet as 'dignified' as if she was entertaining in her own drawing-room instead of in a storm-tossed cabin.

The voyage lasted from 7 a.m. on 7th September until 7 a.m. on the 8th.

Meanwhile, what of the Emperor? Disillusioned, defeated, broken in spirit and suffering dire bodily agony, he sat reviewing all possibilities of renewing the contest.

In his hour of distress, came Bismarck, who with remorseless logic, laid bare the full tragedy of the situation. Only one thing was possible to save the shattered remnants of the Army.

CAPITULATION – Napoleon realized to the full the bitter agony which swept the soul of his great ancestor after Waterloo.

CAPITULATION – It meant the end of all his bright visions, the end of all his fond hopes for France, the end of all his ambitions for his son.

It seems strange, how distorted a picture survives, of the character of the Emperor, Napoleon III.

He may have had many weaknesses, but his stronger qualities outbalanced these.

He was essentially an honest man, those who knew him intimately realized that his aim was not his own glory but the amelioration of his people.

He was clever, deeper than the majority and feared by the Statesmen of Europe, who could not fathom his mind.

All those close to him at Court realized his greatness; like other great men he made mistakes but he was kind, and never expressed a vengeful thought.

Wearily Napoleon took up the pen and signed the terms of surrender, then, surrounded by Prussian guards, he went on his way to Wilhelmhohe – a prisoner.

11 AN ENGLISH HARBOUR

The differing reactions of various personalities in times of great strain and emotion have always interested me.

I knew quite well, many of those charming people who surrounded the Empress, when she was at the height of her glory.

I was young so perhaps it was only natural that I longed to know the part they played, when they had to prove their devotion to the woman who had given them so much, and who now could offer so little.

I learnt of the courage and self-denial displayed by some, but, alas! many sought only their own salvation, and deserted the Empress in her hour of need.

The one who stands out far above all, is Pauline, Princesse Metternich, who although a foreigner, followed the Empress to England, bringing with her La Valette and Rouher.

On hearing that Eugénie had reached Hastings, the energetic Princesse rushed there to find the Empress and her son in a dismal, cold room, coughing and shivering with fever. She realized that something must be done at once.

Calling Dr. Evans and Madame Lebreton aside, she told them that they must set to work immediately to find a suitable house.

In a very short time, almost miraculously, Camden Place was discovered; a few days later the Empress spent her first night in her new home.

The next morning, Eugénie rose early. It was a Sunday; she wanted to give thanks for so much, so she went to the little village church. Somehow, apart from all the sadness which was filling her heart, a sudden oppression seemed to envelop her.

A pain, as if a parting had taken place. What was it?

Eugénie rose from the rush chair she was occupying near the door; when she arrived there was no place for her, so she sat amongst the poorest of the poor.

That night after dinner, she opened the newspaper, then she knew that the pain she had felt in church was the forerunner of the one she was experiencing now – Merimée was dead. He had died at Cannes the previous day.

On the 30th November, 1879, there was a feeling of excitement mingled with grateful astonishment.

Since her arrival from France, Eugénie had pondered anxiously on the reaction of Queen Victoria to her presence in England.

At last, the answer had come. The Queen had announced her approaching visit.

The Empress felt that she might break down, memories of the days when they met as equals flooded into her mind; now she felt almost a pariah, intruding where she had no rightful claim.

She informed her household and told her son to be prepared to receive the Sovereign of Great Britain.

In the early hours of the afternoon, the Queen, accompanied by Princess Beatrice, attended by Lady Ely and Lord Charles Fitzroy, drove up to the door.

The Empress in a simple black gown moved forward with the Prince Imperial to receive Her Majesty; the Court stood in the background.

The Queen alighted from her carriage and greeted the Empress; together they walked into the drawing-room. The first moments of this poignant meeting were difficult, the Empress felt very *émotionée* and yet dreaded to say anything which might be tactless. As they sat in that rather banal drawing-room, only redeemed by some remnants retrieved from France, Eugénie told her august visitor of that last dread day in the Tuileries.

'Madame, the night before I had lain down fully dressed on my bed, but General Trochu administered the final blow when he allowed the Chambers to be taken possession of by the populace.

'There were no troops, the gardens of the Tuileries were overrun by the mob.

'Your Majesty, you will believe me, I had to go. It was a dagger of agony in my heart that I made the decision offering my future to Almighty God – I left my beloved Tuileries.

'Your Majesty knows the rest, Sir John Burgoyne wrote the details of that ghastly crossing to Colonel Ponsonby.'

The little Prince Imperial, just fourteen years of age, stood erect during the whole visit; he was receiving the Queen of England.

A small Court soon gathered round the Empress. The Duc and Duchesse de Mouchy, Princesse Murat, Comtesse Clery, Madame de Saule, the Conneaus, Pietri and Filon were always with her.

In the surrounding district the Duc and Duchesse de Bassano, the Aquados and Davilliers found accomodation, and not far away were the Duchesse de Talleyrand, Princesse de Tarente, the Chevreaus and Rouhers. These were faithful indeed, and a great solace to the Empress in these days of anxiety, but it was left to the Princesse Pauline to discover that nobody had considered the matter of finance. She collected the jewels that she had been instrumental in smuggling out of France and handed them back to Eugénie, at the same time offering a substantial sum of money as a temporary loan.

Having reigned for ten years as Queen of Fashion in Paris, the Princesse felt that she could no longer live there after the fall of the Empire, so she returned with her husband to Vienna, where she found a congenial world in which to forget the sorrows she had witnessed.

Speedily she became the leader of Society, ranking only second to the Imperial family.

Her *salon* was the centre of both the artistic and aristocratic world; by her benevolence she earned for herself the title of *La Princesse Charité*.

The Princesse Mathilde was at her home in rue de Courcelles on the morning of 5th September. Situated as it was in a quiet street, some distance from the Tuileries, the tumult of the previous night had not reached her ears.

She knew, of course, that Paris was seething with discontent, but did not realize the true state of things.

Suddenly Alexandre Dumas *fils* arrived, and asked if she would receive him.

It was still early, the Princesse was in her dressing-gown, so she sent word that he was to come up to her boudoir.

Seeing that he was in a great state of agitation, she asked him what was the matter, then without any preparation, he told her that the Empress had left the Tuileries the previous evening for an unknown destination.

'Madame la Princesse, you too must leave at once.'

She hesitated and said:

'I must wait for Nieuwekerke and take his advice. I am rather anxious,' she added, 'he went out to dinner last evening and has not yet returned.'

Then Alexandre gently took her hand:

'Madame la Princesse, his carriage passed me at the Octroi and I hear that he is on his way to Italy.'

A few hours later, the Princesse, heart-broken at being thus deserted by her lover of the past twenty years, was on her way to Brussels.

It was not long before she was able to return to Paris.

Her friendship with Thiers enabled her to reopen her *salon*, this time in the rue de Berri; as before, her house was reminiscent of the Empire and adorned with Napoleonic relics.

Here she entertained the most varied elements of Society, artists, diplomats, princes and even *députés* of the Republic; in the midst of these, the Princesse reigned supreme.

Comte Walewski, former ambassador at the Court of St. James's, latterly Président of the *Sénat* died in 1868; his widow, the captivating Florentine, one time friend of the Empress, forfeited that friendship when Eugénie discovered that she had been so indiscreet as to encourage Napoleon's flirtations until they ended in something more serious.

At the fall of the Empire, the Comtesse fled to Brussels, where she continually, but uselessly intrigued for the return of the Emperor.

Thiers, now President of the Republic, invited her to Paris and awarded her a pension in consideration of the late Comte's services to the nation.

In later years, she married a certain Conté d'Allesandro. The rest of her life was spent in retirement.

Mélanie de Pourtalès, who from the first foresaw the Prussian menace and attempted to awaken the Emperor to the danger, did all in her power to ameliorate the lot of the Imperial family.

She visited Chislehurst in 1873, and saw the straits to which they were reduced. Returning to Paris, she pleaded with Thiers for the restitution of their personal property, eventually she was successful.

Many years later when I knew Madame de Pourtalès, she always reminded me of a rare *objet d'art*, perhaps a Saxe figurine, exuding all that wonderful charm with which life had endowed her, a life in which surrounded by men's adoration, they had sought to gratify her faintest whim.

I loved driving to the rue Tronchet; although I was young and she already old, she knew that I was the sister of Fanita de Fitz-James, and to me she could talk of Charles de Fitz-James.

In her great red *salon*, hung with pictures by Rembrandt and Van Dyck, she received Kings and Queens, princes and commoners, radiating a feminine charm which seemed, even then, to cast a net of attraction, which none could escape.

Prince Napoleon, always a critic and frequently an opponent of Napoleon III, withdrew first to Switzerland, then to London.

He never participated in the Emperor's optimistic hope of a speedy return to France and a second *coup d'état*!

When the Emperor died, the Prince schemed to become the head of the Imperialist party, but Eugénie who considered herself still Regent for her son fought his claim strenuously until the death of the Prince Imperial.

Thus were scattered far and wide, those who formed the entourage of the Empress.

For most it can be said, that once the Empress had passed from their midst, they ceased to shine as bright planets.

There were exceptions who would have shone in any milieu, Princesse Pauline, Mélanie de Pourtalès and others.

Fortune was kinder to the women than to the men; the latter sank with the Empire they had served and preferred this to serving the new Republic.

Sorrow softens the human heart; this may sound *banal* but very frequently it is a truism.

Six months had gone by since the day that the Empress left the Tuileries for the last time, it was 20th March, 1871, when she stood in her drawing-room at Chislehurst, awaiting the arrival of the Emperor.

Her outlook on the world had changed. She had suffered, so had he. Had he erred, or had she been wrong in her judgment?

Anyhow, it all seemed so long ago; almost in another life. Empress seemed but an empty title now. Her husband, the father of her child, was returning from captivity, it was as such that she welcomed him home. Alas, it was not for long, a few months of restless intrigue and futile plans, then for him the end.

On 3rd January, 1873, Napoleon placed himself in the hands of his surgeons, his agony was so great that nothing else mattered; on 9th January, Napoleon III, Emperor of the French, was no more.

A few days later Eugénie wrote to her mother:

Under the blow of such a terrible sorrow I have not had the courage to write to you even one word. I cannot even today analyse the immense loss we have sustained but I wished you to know that my first thought was for you.

My son is as well as possible, so am I.

Your devoted and unhappy daughter,

EUGÉNIE

The Prince Imperial, upon whose person the hopes of so many were now centred, was just seventeen. Small in stature, he resembled his father, but his features were less accentuated. The Prince had the charming blue eyes of the Empress, he held himself very erect but had a little mannerism of which he was quite unconscious: he would frequently give a tug to his coat as if to straighten it.

He had all the resilience of youth: at one moment he would be discussing a problem of intricate political economy, much beyond his age, a few minutes later he would be leaping the fence round the lawn like an eager boy.

His love and veneration for his father's memory was touching: sometimes, it would slightly irritate the Empress as her love for him had become jealously enveloping.

When the days were bright and clear, and the east wind had dispersed the mists in the Channel, he would go alone to Dover, climb on to the high cliffs and gaze steadfastly to the coast of France, as it lay there across the water like an unattainable dream.

He would sit on those grassy heights preparing in his mind vast plans for the day when his country would acclaim him Napoleon IV.

In the evening when he returned to Camden Place, the Prince would appear sad and thoughtful, none would ask him why, but all could guess.

His was such a short life; so many dreams, so many hopes, so soon to be crushed.

Is it a coincidence or a curse, that since the year 1643, when Louis XIV, still a child, succeeded his father Louis XIII, no direct heir has ascended the throne of France?

Louis XV, Louis XVI, the Dauphin, Napoleon I, the King of Rome, Louis XVIII, Charles X, Louis Philippe, and the Prince Imperial follow one another like a rosary of tragedy.

To me, there is a great analogy between the lives of the King of Rome and the Prince Imperial; they both lost their father when still young, but for them their memory never faded, it endured as the impulse and inspiration of their young lives.

The King of Rome could not recall his father's features, but, notwithstanding all the measures employed to efface the image from his heart, it never dimmed with the passing years but rather strengthened with his longing to return to France.

As his health gradually failed, not a word from his beloved country was allowed to reach him to assuage his anguish. So, in the splendour of Schoenbrunn, when the last days drew near, and he lay on the Imperial bed of Austria, *soi-disant* an Austrian Prince, as they called him, Duc de Reichstadt, a title he would never acknowledge, in the silence of his heart, he faintly murmured:

'*Vous voulez dire le Roi de Rome.*'

In many ways the story of the son of Napoleon III resembles that of his cousin, the son of Napoleon I.

The years had passed, events had happened, the young man who still was named the Prince Imperial, was living at Camden Place, a mileu less sumptuous than Schoenbrunn, exuding all the atmosphere of a home, but still a house of exile. Napoleon III was dead, the Prince seemed to exist only in the shadow of his father's memory like the King of Rome, his father was his *raison d'être* and France his 'Mecca'.

The great difference between the lives of the two *heritiers* lay in the fact that the Prince Imperial passed his life amidst followers whose whole existence was centred in the restoration of the Dynasty – his cousin lived in an alien court; but still each young man brooded as he listened to the schemes and intrigues.

Both were determined to follow their own plans.

Charles de Fitz-James told me that once, when he was in England for the shooting season, he went to Chislehurst to pay his respects to the Empress before he returned to France.

They had not met for many years; with each turn of the wheels which brought his train nearer to its destination, his heart grew fainter with apprehension of what he might find.

A carriage met him at the station, slowly the country seemed to glide past as he drove to Camden Place.

The house appeared to his eyes just a large, very ordinary mansion, and as he stepped into the hall, it looked simple and lacking in luxury.

While he waited to be announced, the strain of meeting his hostess seemed to augment. Then, upstairs a door opened and shut suddenly, a well-remembered voice called:

'Poché. Poché, *mon ami!*' and the Empress came down the stairs.

Charles told me that, at first, he could hardly see her, his eyes had filled with tears, but he masked his emotion and fell on one knee. As he kissed her hand, she bent down to him and just touched his forehead with her lips. For some moments, neither spoke, then taking his arm, the Empress passed with him into the drawing-room. For a long time, they could find no words to begin the conversation. Then the Empress with a mischievous smile, murmured:

'This is not quite as grand as the last room in which we met' (referring to the Tuileries).

From that moment, the ice was broken and it seemed as though they would never cease from their recollections.

113

At length, the door opened, and a young man came in. Charles stood up and wondered whom he could be.

The Empress said: '*Mon fils.*'

Charles gasped – when last he had seen him some nine years before, the Prince was still a small boy, now he stood before him, Napoleon's son – his Emperor, Napoleon IV.

He certainly had a strong look of his father, but he was smaller and more delicate looking.

The Empress asked Charles to remain to dinner. She excused his not dressing; to prevent him feeling awkward she sent word 'nobody need change tonight'.

Later, when the Empress had retired to rest before dinner, Charles met his old friends, but all the time the Prince Imperial hovered around. At last, he whispered:

'Monsieur de Fitz-James, I should like to have a talk with you.'

So he and Charles went out into the garden and sat on a seat.

Then the young boy turned to him and said:

'Tell me all you remember of my father in the Tuileries.'

They sat and sat until the time arrived for dinner, then the Prince thanked him and said:

'Do not leave too soon after dinner, there is something I wish to show you.'

When, at length, Charles had taken leave of the Empress, the Prince whispered, 'Remember you are to come with me,' then taking his arm, he said to the Court:

'Monsieur de Fitz-James will be back in half an hour.'

When they were alone, the Prince said:

'I am sure you loved and respected my father. You have proved it by the manner in which you have spoken of him today, so I want to show you the most sacred spot I possess.'

Saying this, he led him into a small room. Charles told me that the furniture was very simple, a wardrobe with endless uniforms as far as he could visualize, it may have been open or had glass doors.

On the floor, a dark carpet, a few pictures on the walls, but dominating the whole room was a huge map of Europe. Somehow, as he looked, France seemed to stand out supreme. A few ordinary knick-knacks lay around, but what struck him most was the kind of camp bed in iron where a few violets lay scattered upon the coverlet.

It was all so unassuming and one wondered why the man who had possessed for nearly a quarter of a century all the luxury the world could provide, should have lived and died in so small a space.

As they were leaving, the Prince who had not uttered a syllable, bowed low before the humble bed and, dipping his finger in a small silver *bénitier* which hung near the door, touched Charles' hand with the holy water and slowly made the Sign of the Cross. So they passed from the room.

Charles felt too moved to meet anyone, so he asked the Prince to take him direct to the carriage which stood waiting at the door.

As he took leave of this young boy, who that day had shown so much heart, and who was capable of so much tenderness, and yet displayed dignity and courage when looking to the future of France, a slight pain gripped his heart and he said:

'*Au revoir, Monseigneur, que Dieu vous garde toujours.*'

He bowed low as the Prince took his hand and said:

'Today you have taught me to honour and love my father and Emperor even more than I did before. *Au revoir*, Monsieur, and if, one day, I require your help, I shall count on your affection.'

'So I left,' Charles told me, 'and I never saw him again but, like the King of Rome, he died a true Frenchman.'

12 END OF AN EMPIRE

At the time that the Zulu War broke out in 1878, the Prince Imperial was a cadet at Woolwich. Daily his comrades were leaving for Africa. He was left behind.

He felt that he was surrounded by intrigue at Camden Place.

Intrigues! Intrigues! Intrigues!

They were driving him mad with their political schemes.

He knew that politics alone would never reunite him to his beloved country. Only acts of valour attached to his name would identify him with the *esprit militaire* which is the soul of France.

He appealed for permission to fight; to the War Office, to the Government, finally, to the Queen.

On 27th February, 1879, he left for South Africa. He dreamed of glory, his courage won him fame. But his glory was short-lived.

The news of the death of the Prince Imperial was telegraphed to Queen Victoria who was in residence at Balmoral at the time.

In her diary she wrote:

> Balmoral,
> *19th June, 1878.*
>
> After dinner Leila Erroll read, and I was writing, when just before eleven o'clock a telegram was given me with the message that it contained bad news.
>
> When I, alarmed, asked what, I was told it was that the Prince Imperial had been killed.
>
> I feel a thrill of horror in writing this. I kept saying, 'No! No! it can't be – to die in such an awful way is too shocking!' Poor Empress, her only child, her all, gone! I am really in despair. He was such an amiable good young man, who would have made such a good Emperor of the French one day. It is a real misfortune. The more one thinks of it the worse it becomes!
>
> Got to bed very late and it was just dawning! and little sleep did I get.

116

A few weeks passed whilst the body was being brought to England in a warship.

The Prince of Wales, deeply distressed by the death of the Prince Imperial, could not do enough to manifest his sympathy.

Orders were given for minute guns to salute the vessel as it passed up the Channel, and the French, despite their change of régime, were pleased at this salute to a scion of the Bonapartes. The Queen hurried from Scotland to Windsor, thence to Camden Place to lay a wreath of laurels on his breast as he lay covered with the entwined flags of France and Britain.

The last sad scene made a deep impression upon Her Majesty, as is evidenced by these extracts from her journal:

> Windsor Castle,
> *12th July, 1879.*

At the door (of Camden Place, Chislehurst) we were met by Lord Sydney, Princesse Mathilde (whom I had not seen since 1855 in Paris), Prince Napoleon, with his two sons Victor and Louis, Prince Lucien Bonaparte (the savant who always resides in England), Prince Charles Napoleon Bonaparte (his nephew), Prince Murat, his daughter Eugénie, and his brother Prince Louis, the Duc de Basasno and others.

We were at once taken into the Chapelle Ardente, which was beautifully arranged, all hung with white and burning candles all around.

On a catafalque, covered with a violet velvet pall, embroidered with golden bees, was placed the coffin on which rested the Order of the Légion d'Honneur and quantities of wreaths – we placed our wreaths and knelt a moment in prayer, and then retired by the same way we came.

We were shown into a rather large room which had been the Emperor's study and which the poor Empress had just arranged for her son.

The Princes, and Princesse Mathilde came in here, and the different Princes were presented by Prince Napoleon, who was very civil, very subdued and embarrassed.

Princesse Mathilde I found very little altered. Prince Napoleon is aged and grown balder, and more like to Napoleon I than ever.

His eldest son Victor is tall and nice and intelligent-looking, very like the Italian family, but with the fine Bonaparte brow and complexion. The second is much shorter and darker, and has quite the Bonaparte features. Prince Lucien is grey and old looking, very pleasing and gentleman-like. He loved the dear young Prince dearly, and feels his death acutely. He is the son of Napoleon I's elder brother. He was present at the painful identification and said: '*Mais je l'ai reconnu.*' When I remarked to Prince Napoleon how dreadful this event was he said, '*C'est bien triste, votre Majesté a été si bonne!*' Princesse Mathilde repeated the same and added, '*Il s'est précipité et a dû avoir l'esprit malade.*' I said: 'I thought he had only had the natural wish to distinguish himself, and *de faire quelque chose.*'

The moment was now fast approaching when what remained of the dear young Prince had to leave his mother's roof for ever! We went into the next room where ladies and gentlemen were waiting with the Marquis de Castelbajac, who had been placed in attendance on me. By pulling up the blinds we could look out upon the entrance where the gun carriage was already drawn up by the door. There was a great assemblage of officers, gentlemen and French gentlemen, the latter in evening dress, standing by, cadets from Woolwich mounting guard. In another few minutes, we saw the coffin borne out by ten artillery officers preceded by the Clergy, one priest carrying the crucifix on high. The muffled drums rolled, the minute guns began to fire. It was a fearfully thrilling affecting moment! The pall bearers (my four sons, George Cambridge, the Crown Prince of Sweden, the Duc de Bassano and Monsieur Rouher) now came out to take their places holding white cords hanging from the gun carriage. We went out and stood at the corner of the house watching the preparations and were then asked to go up to a raised covered seat from whence we could witness the sad procession.

In a few moments all was ready to start. First came 200 Military cadets, to whom was given (in remembrance of the Prince having been one himself), the special honour of forming the Escort, marching in columns of four with arms reversed. The Royal Artillery Band, with muffled drums continually rolling, playing the fearfully solemn, wailing and too well-known Dead March in Saul, the ten R.A. Officers who had carried the coffin and placed it on the gun carriage, the Clergy, including the Bishop (of Constantinople) who wore his Mitre which had a very fine effect; then suddenly appeared the gun carriage drawn by six horses bearing its sad and precious freight.

The coffin was covered and beautifully arranged with the two flags of England and France, and wreaths of flowers, including my laurel one which, as I had wished, had a conspicuous place. Two artillerymen sat in front holding the dear Empress' beautiful wreath of white flowers. Immediately behind the gun carriage came the dear Prince's horse entirely caparisoned in black and gold led by Mr. Gamble, the late Emperor's stud groom who had been with him in England in 1855, had followed him here in 1871 and had remained with the Prince Imperial. The two poor servants (Uhlmann, the Prince's faithful valet who had been with him since his birth, and the soldier servant Lomas, who went out with the Prince); then followed Prince Bonaparte, his sons and the rest of the Bonaparte family (all wearing the 'Légion d'Honneur'), Christian, young Prince of Baden, Franz Teck, Ernest Leiningen, Edward Weimar, Victor Gleichen and Louis Battenberg, besides an immense number of British Generals, Colonel Stanley, Sir M. H. Beach, next to whom came numbers and numbers of French.

It was a most beautiful, touching, solemn procession and yet not gloomy.

After it had left the grounds, the band took up that beautiful and most sad March of Beethoven's. Nearly 2,000 people passed in one unceasing stream. Almost, if not all French of every class, all bearing violets and carrying wreaths, also banners brought over from France.

We occasionally caught glimpses of the sad procession winding its way across the Common. The music died gradually away, and when the minute gun ceased firing, we knew that the procession had reached the Church.

The Duchesse de Mouchy had joined us after a little while, and was very much affected. She said the Empress was in a dreadful state, each gun seemed to shake her through and through, which I could quite understand as they are fearful, combined with the solemn music and muffled drums! When everyone had passed, we went back into the house. Monsieur de Castelbajac said as we went in: *'L'intérêt est fini, il ne reste plus que le sentiment.'*

Madame Aguado and Mlle de Larmenât came to say the Empress had got up again to see me, so we hastened up, and I went into the little room where I saw her last. It was in such complete darkness that I could not in the least see where she was. She came towards me and sobbed much, and when I put my arms round her, telling her no one felt for her as I did, she gently said: *'Je vous remercie, Madame, pour toutes vos bontés.'*

She asked if Beatrice was there and kissed her also, then we left the room. This is the end of all that was once so brilliant, and of one who promised not only to his Country but to the World. He bore truly the 'white flower of a blameless life.'

We got back after one o'clock. Arthur showed me a letter from Captain Lane, he was one of those who went out to find the poor dear Prince's body. He gives a short account of it, and sent Arthur a little bit of the Prince's hair which he cut off thinking I might like to have it.

The Second Empire was over. With the death of the Prince Imperial all hopes of the restoration of the Empire ceased. For the present we must leave the Empress. We shall return again to take up the life of the French capital, a Paris still gay but reflecting the ever-changing mood of the New Republic.

PART TWO

13 RENDEZ-VOUS MOULIN ROUGE

The fall of the Second Empire, sad though it was to its close adherents, was not a total collapse of their way of life. General Fleury effectively summed up the whole matter and pronounced the epitaph of the régime when he said:

'*Sans doute, c'est triste, mais tout de même nous nous sommes diablement amusés.*'

During the nineteenth century, France had seen dynasties rise and fall, but despite this, the followers of these régimes had continued to live in Paris and move in Society, each in their own particular circle, totally ignoring the very existence of rival cliques, even that of the Government in power.

So it was, after the disaster at Sedan, the siege of Paris, the tumults of the Commune and even the humiliation of the march of the Prussian Army down the Champs-Élysées through the Arc de Triomphe, left the people completely unmoved.

The Spirit of Paris emerged from these troublous times unconquered, still gay and frivolous.

I remember reading somewhere, 'It would take a genie to destroy the spirit of France, and even he could not entirely succeed.'

The French paid the huge war indemnity in record time, established the Republic, then, having set their house in order, resumed normal life as though there had been no interruption.

Indeed, in some respects, life had continued normally, even during the dark days of the Siege.

Artists had gone on with their work in the ateliers of Montmartre, true their food was rather more weird than usual; cats, dogs, even rats found their way into the casserole, but Cézanne, Van Gogh, Pissarro and their disciples continued to paint, though the glass in the windows rattled, and fell in pieces with the thunder of the guns.

I well remember the signboard of a certain butcher at the top of the boulevard Haussmann on which was painted a large elephant, to recall the fact that he had bought the elephant from the *Jardin des plantes* during the Siege, and sold its carcass in joints to the starving citizens.

In the *Académie des Sciences*, Pasteur continued his experiments regarding it as his sacred duty to humanity.

Sully Prudhomme, Dumas *fils* and Victor Hugo produced works breathing sentiments of devotion and hope.

Even the proclamation of the German Empire in the Salle des Mirroirs at Versailles made no forcible impact upon the mental outlook.

Really it was no affair of theirs, so the people of Paris went about their own business, carefully avoiding those streets likely to be used by the Prussians, simply ignoring, as far as possible, their very existence.

From the days of the Middle Ages, the Quartier Latin has been the centre of culture, not only for Paris, but for the whole civilized world.

In the thirteenth century, Pope Alexander IV said:

'Paris fills the universe with the wealth of its learning and reveals to the world the secrets of knowledge.'

In those days, the Church held the monopoly of intellect, and students flocked to Paris from every country. Latin was their only common tongue, the language of their religion, hence the name Quartier Latin.

Here it was, on Mont St. Geneviève in the early thirteenth century, that the first college of Theology was founded by Robert de Sorbonne, Confessor to St. Louis; to this very day the University of Paris bears his honoured name.

The Quartier Latin with its narrow streets, ancient buildings and *hôtels meublés* was the home of the students, here too were to be found the 'Bohemian' and the 'Grisette' whose doings have played so great a part in many an opera.

Haussmann destroyed much of the charm of the neighbourhood when he pierced its vitals with the Boulevard St. Michel, the rue des Écoles and rue Guy Lussac, but as the years passed even these in their turn became famous in story and song.

The 'Boul Mich' is not only the shopping centre, but a popular promenade of student life at all hours of the day and night.

Here in the cheap cafés, Verlaine, Maupassant and others spent their time talking the evening through, often far into the night.

Near the 'Boul Mich' are the gardens of the Luxembourg, refuge of lovers to whom the dusk is kind.

There is one shop in the Quartier which must be haunted by many a sad spirit.

Flammarion's for generations has been a beloved *rendez-vous*; here one can buy books, pens, paper and ink, all that it needed to achieve eternal fame, if one could only express on paper the burning aspirations of a soul.

In its kindly shadows one can browse for hours, reading some book one cannot afford to buy, no one will disturb you, *C'est la loi*.

Flammarion's Arcade was the haunt of Victor Hugo, and Anatole France, of Fargue, Valery and Gide; here too came those others, the unfortunates, the unknown, whose master-pieces conceived in such agony never lived to astonish the world.

The Quartier Latin and Montmartre are poles apart, one the realm of paper and ink, the other a world where canvas and brush are supreme.

The very air of Montmartre seems to carry the seeds of neglect, untidyness and sloth; there is a feeling of *insouciance*, a medley of hard work, leisure, laughter and tears. This is the very essence of the district.

As one climbs the rue Caulincourt, or indeed any of the smaller streets, one can sense the life pulsing so vigorously all around you.

Hark! There is the cry of the *marchand d'habits* who, dressed in discoloured overcoat, with three hats piled on his head, is pushing his rickety barrow of very second-hand clothes. His clients come running hopefully from the doorways, garments in hand, which they seek to sell for a few sous.

Students clatter down the stairs, willing to sell the very coat off their back if it may purchase the price of a meal or enough to take their mistress of the moment to *L'Ely de Montmartre*.

As the old man rounds the corner and disappears from view, other cries are heard. The *vitrier* who comes to mend the window panes broken in last night's quarrel, then the old wreck selling groundsel and crying, '*le mouron pour les petits oiseaux*'.

Students emerge from the houses on their way to the ateliers of their different *maîtres*. Some of these are elegant, others intent on appearing artistically untidy in their velvet coats with their *bérets* posed at an angle of studied indifference.

Mingling with the men are women, some lovely young girls, alas already tainted, but hoping to keep out of hospital; others, old hags bent double from stooping over the tubs of soapy water amidst which they spend their lives.

The atmosphere reeks with the stench from the drainless houses, redolent of decay.

Yet, despite all this, there is an indescribable charm, born of the friendliness and sympathy of the people. All are willing to help one another in time of difficulty and in the daily routine of life.

If an artist is fortunate enough to sell a picture, he will buy some little delicacy for his *concièrge* or her children, then call his friends together for a celebration.

The studios are mostly *greniers*, attics located in the top floor of old battered buildings, smelling of mildew and reached by climbing precariously up a rickety stair, whose banister has long been smashed and whose steps are uneven and worn.

The walls are stained with damp and grease from constant use.

Yet these garrets are eagerly sought after as places where work can be done and fame pursued.

In such a room, a group of friends would meet to discuss one of the two eternal topics, art or women.

The only furniture might be a few broken chairs, whose damaged legs were supported on a pile of books. A piece of matting in front of the iron stove which filled one corner, its pipe going through the dingy ceiling, to God knows where. This was the only source of warmth and sometimes if one was hard up, of light as well; on it was done the cooking of the meagre meals.

The window took up the whole of one side of the room; frequently several panes were broken, rags and paper being stuffed into the cavities; on the ledge an anaemic plant struggled for survival.

The owner of this room might be displaying his latest canvas; his friends standing around smoking pipes or cheap cigars, leaning against the walls or lolling in the chairs, their velveteen jackets stained with paint, their flowing ties and coloured waistcoats soiled by tobacco ash.

Overhead, a cord near the sagging ceiling bore the weekly wash.

His model, or perhaps his mistress (frequently she was both), would stand near the stove, clad in a soiled and flimsy dressing-gown, feet encased in flapping slippers, her hair roughly coiled on the top of her head; probably she would be stewing a 'ragout' in a saucepan over the stove.

Near the easel usually stood a small table, with jam jars full of brushes, a palette, and several tubes of paint, amongst which you could find a bottle of wine half empty, a loaf of bread, some mouldy cheese and a plate of fruit.

If we could look through the window, we should see nothing but sky and roofs. Roofs of houses similar to this with broken tiles, crooked chimneys; the only sign of life, a couple of pigeons bowing and cooing to one another their eternal song of love.

In the attic, the air would be tense with excitement – would the picture on which their all is staked be accepted for the *salon*; if so, they were made, if not?

Many would work on for a while in spite of rejection, in the hope that one day, they might be acclaimed as great artists.

But, waiting meant funds. So often, disappointed and broken, they would shut the studio door for the last time, leaving in the empty room their shattered hopes to mingle with the ghosts of former dreams.

Perhaps solace might be sought at l'Élysée de Montmartre, the famous night haunt of the Quartier then in the height of its glory, and affectionately known by the students as 'l'Ély'.

Au fond it was awful, sordid and unhealthy, but it had no rival, and there one could find forgetfulness in drink or women, or both.

Drink was cheap, women were cheaper. They would dance, kiss or do anything, so what more could a penniless student desire.

There they gathered in crowds to laugh and sip their *vin chaud* or pernod and perchance seek oblivion for their sorrows.

Here too was La Goulue, who was then at the height of her fame. Originally, she was one of the many washerwomen of the Quartier. She was young and fair, her face attractive, but not good looking, was typical of the Apache underworld. Short in stature, her hair pulled up on the top of her head and fastened in a knob. Every movement of her body as she danced the *cancan*, was an invitation to vice.

At l'Ély everything was permitted, the habituées being a law unto themselves, all decency was cast aside; half of this was simply high spirits, the other shameless intensions; but to all these men and girls it was a means of release, a self-expression.

As they usually passed their time in the studios studying the nude, what difference did a few clothes make, what matter if in dancing they showed the rest.

The period of the eighties and nineties was an epoch of madness. Immorality is too weak a word to describe the life of some of the well-known artists and poets of Montmartre and the Quartier Latin. Of those obscure geniuses who lived and died unknown, nobody cared what kind of life was theirs. Many lasted but a few years, dragging out a miserable existence in hunger and poverty, dying of neglect and starvation.

Whilst they lived, they hoped and toiled for recognition, sacrificing all in the pursuit of fame.

The cemeteries in the *banlieus* of the city are filled with the graves of these unfortunate youths and girls who led a hectic life, squandering their miserable pittance in wild debauch, the rest of the time they were cold and hungry in their garrets. At length came the awful hour, when hope failed and they trudged with faltering step to the Seine, a last pause on the bridge, then a leap; soon the waters flowed on placidly, scarcely disturbed by the body which had fallen into their depths.

There were those who became notorious as well as famous, men like Toulouse Lautrec, Verlaine, Baudelaire and Maupassant.

Their lives, to me, seem the saddest of all. It was as though they were at birth endowed with dual natures, and the Gods, jealous that mortals should be gifted with such divine fire, had sought to outweigh their creative ideals with the weakness and vice of human frailty.

Of all these unbalanced souls, whose minds rejected the conventions which hedge the path of life, Toulouse Lautrec was the most poignant figure. Crippled and hideously ugly, ever seeking love, always to be rebuffed. Full of the emotions and longings of other men, yet frustrated – even the street-walkers would refuse and say, 'Ah! No! You are too ugly!' – gradually the truth dawned on him that he was a monster.

He tried to forget in orgies and drink, but oblivion eluded his grasp, even as love had done. His pictures reflected the agony of his soul, and were a mirror of his passions. People mentioned his name with a shudder, but could not deny his power of so vividly portraying the decadence of human nature.

He excelled in depicting a certain type of old *mackrelle* and their victims, young girls who already knew life to the full, and were a source of income to these old hags – procuresses in the *cancan* of life.

When the end drew near, he went home to die. As the long days dragged by, the awful past seemed but a nightmare born of the hours of darkness. He received the last Sacraments, and in the bed where he had slept as an innocent child, death came as a blessed relief.

Another of that brilliant group was the poet, Verlaine. How pathetic was his wasted existence.

It seemed as though there was a taint of 'atavism' which swayed his long life of debauchery, yet we can glimpse an innate beauty in the darkness of his soul.

His verse, delicate and exquisite in its phrasing and tone value, breathes a longing for purity, tenderness for his mother and remorse for the anguish he caused her. Truly a strange exotic genius: he underwent two years of imprisonment for a murderous attack on his best friend Rimbaud, and emerged a changed man, converted and redeemed.

Maupassant, another of this wild but gifted brotherhood, spent his days passing from one excess to another, only to end in the horrible shadows of the madhouse.

Baudelaire, the boon companion of many a libertine, the centre of the vilest orgies, composed some of the most beautiful verse ever written in the French language.

He also in his latter days became reconciled with the Church and ended as almost a religious fanatic.

The exquisite poetry of François Coppée might be described as profanely chaste; his early works in particular exude a delicate sensuality, expressing as they do, the emotions of a young student struggling with life.

He sees daily the little *midinette* passing on her way to work, their glances meet, love triumphs.

To me, his verse recalls the beauty of a Chopin prelude.

As one wanders the winding streets of Montmartre, and the Quartier Latin, the ghosts of these long dead romantics seem to linger in the shadows, reluctant to depart from the scene of their inspiration.

Amidst all this life of folly and frivolity, where so many lived but for the immediate moment, and flirtation, money and intrigue were the only things that counted; others passed a very different existence.

Theirs was a hidden life, of their self-sacrifice of which the world at large never knew or cared.

They were gay, witty and elegant, shining amidst the social throng, often amongst the last to leave a ball or reception; this was only one side of their life.

Returning home, they would snatch a few hours sleep, then start out on their secret mission. A heavily laden basket on their arm, they would visit the needy, leaving food or medicine, cheering the downcast, lifting those who had fallen by the wayside, cleaning filthy rooms, washing the sick, dressing children and so on from house to house – facing contagion and disease, but like the Saints fearing nothing.

Soeur Génevieve, a Sister of St. Vincent de Paul, told me of their work, saying:

'You see, *Madame la Baronne*, these ladies and gentlemen are really saints.'

As she said that, I could not help thinking that despite their great charity, these ladies and gentlemen had their times of rest and leisure; but what of her Order, the members of which worked ceaselessly day and night.

The Soeurs de St. Vincent de Paul and the Petites Soeurs Servantes des Pauvres were a feature of Paris; unlike their imitators, their rule never relaxed.

Whilst all around, men and women were dancing endlessly

and, shall I say, uselessly, to the music of the violins, these heroic nuns left their hard straw palliasses at four o'clock in the morning.

When the world was seeking its bed, they were hearing Mass, and receiving, in Holy Communion, the One who would sustain them through the long day of toil and suffering.

The nuns would then start out on their errands of mercy, carrying huge bags, too heavy for their tired and aching limbs.

They spent the whole day climbing rickety stairs, comforting the dying and succouring the helpless. In epidemics, in sorrow or joy, always bringing with them love and charity, daily offering their toil and labour to the glory of God.

The Little Sisters of the Poor are not even permitted to accept a glass of water; their life is one long sequence of giving, but never taking.

If they had time, they would hurry back to the convent for food, but often it happened that they would spend the whole day without anything passing their lips not even a sip of water.

Sometimes I accompanied Soeur Génevieve on her depressing round.

One day, overcome by her saintliness, I said:

'My dear Sister, you are too good.'

She looked so utterly astonished, that I stumbled over my next words fearing that I had disturbed something almost too holy for this world.

'I mean, your whole life spent in utter self-abnegation, never giving a thought to yourself, even for a second.'

'It is you, Madame, who are good,' she replied.

'But Sister I do so little,' I responded, rather regretfully.

'That is just why! Much is expected of us, our responsibility is almost terrifying, we have promised so much, whilst you who are in the world, promise nothing, so whatever good you do is much greater than ours.'

I found myself speechless, but I have often thought of her words.

Although the Tuileries were now only a heap of ruins and the brilliancy of St. Cloud, Compiègne and Fontainebleau were extinct, those who had been a part of it all could not mourn for ever, so in the despised atmosphere of the Republic they continued to entertain.

Amongst the ladies of Society at that time, none equalled the Princesse de Sagan.

As there was no longer a Court, it soon came to pass that to be received in the *salons* of a few of the *grandes dames*, was to acquire a status similar to that given by presentation at Court.

The Princesse de Sagan, apart from her great fortune, had become a leading figure of European Society, receiving all the great notabilities who graced the French Capital.

She knew her power, and she had the art of keeping the limelight focused on her name.

One day, she allowed a slight rumour to spread.

'*Is it true* that the Princesse de Sagan might be giving a ball?'

A week later:

'The Princesse de Sagan *is* thinking of giving a ball.'

And the following week:

'The Princesse de Sagan *is* giving a fancy dress ball.'

Then the agony began. Whom would she invite? whom leave out?

Women suffered mental torment daily, men did the same; but they adopted a debonair attitude, as if the very thought of receiving one of the coveted invitations had never entered their mind; in secret, both sexes consulted illustrated histories, and visited art galleries, so as not to be devoid of ideas if the longed-for card arrived.

If by some mischance they met, they would immediately stand before the nearest landscape, as though historical costume was the furthest thing from their mind.

In those feverish days of preparation before the ball, I really think if one had listened carefully one would surely have heard the whirring of countless sewing machines, and the laboured breath of the numbers of *midinettes* as they sewed fine seams in silk, satin and lace to create the fabulous costumes worn that evening.

Let us try to take part, if only in imagination, in that wonderful entertainment.

None, in their wildest dreams, could have pictured beforehand, the truly Oriental scene.

My mother and sisters who were amongst the chosen guests, told me that as their carriage drove into the vast courtyard of the Hôtel de Sagan, their eyes were dazzled by the thousands of fairy lights gleaming in the garden beyond; they seemed to out-number the very leaves on the trees on that lovely evening in June.

As they entered the mansion, footmen in blue and gold livery with powdered wigs, stood holding huge five-branched silver candelabra.

Like statues, they posed motionless lining the steps of the huge marble stairway leading to the dais, where six slender columns supported a golden dome under which lay the Princesse on a divan. Stalwart Nubian slaves stood fanning their mistress with long plumed fans.

The Princesse was dressed in a fantastic Oriental robe, literally covered with precious stones. On her fair hair was a monumental head-dress of glittering plumes sparkling with rubies and tur-quoise, from which fell a veil of spangled gauze.

As each guest passed before her, the ladies made a deep reverence, the men bowed low and kissed her hand.

When all had arrived, they formed into groups, the costumes of each being of the same period, and moved in stately procession to the music of a polonaise, before the throne of their hostess.

Later, escorted by her Nubians waving high their fans, she proceeded to the ballroom, where all had gathered; then the double doors were flung wide, and there entered a perfect galaxy of beauty in Louis Seize costumes to dance the quadrilles with which the ball opened.

How beautiful were the women, how gallant the men, and how perfectly they danced; chosen for their figures and good looks, they made a lovely picture.

The first quadrille was danced by partners all arrayed in the palest pastel blue; the second in pink; the third in white and the last in old gold. Truly it was as though Sèvres figurines had come to life, or a Watteau picture become a reality.

Phantasy and wealth had vied to achieve originality and splendour.

Suddenly in the midst of this bewildering feast of colour and rhythm, there appeared a beautiful foreigner, a Belgian, whose costume was so simple, that it made a startling contrast.

As she approached the Princesse it was seen that she wore only a very thin white gauze, through which every limb of her lovely body was visible.

Around her tiny waist was an iron girdle, her delicate wrists were fastened by long chains to her ankles, her perfectly shaped feet were bare, her long dark hair fell around her like a mantle.

She was famous in Paris for her beauty, the chained slave must soon have found a master.

At midnight, silver trumpets sounded a fanfare announcing supper.

The Marquise de Gallifet, wife of the famous general, stood at the golden gates of the *salon*, representing the Archangel Michael. She wore huge feathered wings and brandished a flaming sword, as she proclaimed:

'We are now to enter Paradise!'

The gates were thrown open, indeed it looked as if nothing greater in the way of delicacies could possibly exist in Paradise itself.

Far into the night, into the early hours of the morning, the festivities went on, women courting admiration and mostly gaining it, husbands and mistresses, wives and lovers flirted and made love, returning to their homes as the dawn broke with memories of the most sumptuous fête ever given in Paris.

The Princesse de Sagan had gained her desire, her ball was unique.

The Paris of Haussmann seemed to act as a magnet to the rest of the world.

From the banks of the far-off Volga, the Vistula or the Danube, a fever seemed to develop which Paris, and only Paris could satisfy.

To these nations it meant encountering women of easy virtue, gambling, eating lobsters.

Autocrats, princes and potentates surged towards this Capital. The Prince of Wales, the Prince of Orange, Paul Demidoff, Nariskhine and others formed a 'circle' which became famous amongst the habitués of the Maison Doré.

Aurelian Scholl once remarked: 'All the joyous company has

disappeared – only one is left, the Prince of Wales and he has turned out badly – he has become a King.'

The Prince of Wales had made no secret of his sympathy with France during those sad days of the war. When the Empress sought refuge in England, he was anxious to place Chiswick House at her disposal, but his kindly gesture was vetoed by the Queen, so, later, was his offer to send corn to the starving people of Paris.

After the withdrawal of the invading armies, the Prince returned to the City which had adopted him as one of its sons.

The palaces were empty, the Tuileries and St. Cloud blackened ruins, but the boulevards and *La rive gauche* lived on.

He loved Paris and Paris adored him; life was gay and women as beautiful as before. *Au fond* Paris was still unique whether ruled by Emperor or President.

The Marquis de Gallifet frequently entertained him in his *appartement*, and he was often to be found dining on the boulevards with a gay party of intimate friends.

He generally travelled as Lord Renfrew, to avoid formalities but his face and figure were unmistakable, and the whisper passed through the City: 'The Prince of Wales is here.'

From a fête to a duel, in those days seemed quite natural. I remember a famous *rencontre* that took place, which is delightfully described by Monsieur André de Fouquières in his book *Cinquante Ans de Panache*.

In France the sense of honour was ever exceedingly delicate, thus duels were almost an everyday occurrence.

Sometimes the dispute arose on a serious matter, at others, the most trivial incident was sufficient to cause the offended person to send his seconds to demand satisfaction. Often one of the adversaries merely sought to gain notoriety, and after an exchange of shots, the combatants were persuaded to shake hands, then they drove away with their seconds and honour was satisfied.

At other times, the duel was fought *à outrance*, and was only terminated when one of the two was seriously wounded.

An episode which might be considered typical but which only one man could have carried off successfully concerned Comte Robert de Montesquiou.

He was a poet and satirical author, who lived at Neuilly in the Pavillon des Muses; when he entertained *en grand Seigneur*; all who counted came to his *salon*, where he led the discussion on themes of literature and art.

His wit was cruel and sharp as a stiletto.

The most famous and perhaps the most theatrical duel of that time was his encounter with Henri Regnier. It all took place on the ridiculous subject of – a walking stick.

Enraged by Montesquiou's bitter remarks, Regnier told him that he was only fit to carry a muff and a fan.

Montesquiou, always seeking publicity, promptly challenged Regnier, and a meeting was arranged.

Before it took place, Montesquiou saw to it that the secret should circulate through Paris. Consequently, when the principals arrived at the meeting place, there was a huge concourse of spectators.

Doctors arrived and laid out their instruments, a lady friend even brought a priest for the last Sacraments.

In dead silence, the duel began. Almost immediately Montesquiou received a scratch, and, much to the disappointment of the crowd, the combat was over almost before it had really begun.

Montesquiou was taken home and lay heavily bandaged in his exquisitely decorated bedroom, where presently all Paris arrived to condole with him on his wound. He told a friend of mine that 'for him, it had been a triumphal fête'.

The story advances to the year 1888 when the Empress passed through Paris on her way to Cap Martin. It is perhaps sad that life is so short? After all, what is a mere span of sixty, seventy or even eighty years: just eighty times twelve months at the most and then it is over – over for ever on this earth. I wonder if it would be a help when in anguish if one could only view it all dispassionately, and realize how brief a space of time lies before us. Thoughts such as these passed through the mind of the Empress Eugénie on that day in 1888, when she looked down from the window of her drawing-room at the Hôtel Continental, on to the gardens of the Tuileries lying bathed in sunshine.

Madame Arcos, her great friend, spoke to my mother of the sentiments to which Eugénie gave utterance, one day during a visit to Paris.

The Empress had suffered much since that evening when Napoleon assured her that she would never be insulted again. Poignant memories of the past were recalled as she gazed at the trees budding forth, the freshly cut grass, the broken and shattered ruins of the palace where once she shone supreme, at the children sailing their boats upon the pond, in the very garden where her child had played, and run with his hoop or fought with his friend Conneau. Where she had stood at a window with the Emperor looking down on the scene, making plans for the Prince's brilliant future.

Now, she was seeing this garden again, but from a *caravanserai* not a palace. All had vanished, husband, son, Merimée, and the very throne from which she had reigned as Empress of a nation which then acclaimed her with delirious adulation, and now did not even recognize her face. When she walked, as she had done that morning, with Madame Arcos amidst the crowd of nurses and children, *midinettes* eating their lunch from a bag of *frites* and throwing a crumb to the pigeons strutting on the gravel, old men sitting on the wooden benches reading their *Petit Journal*, none of these even lifted their head as the Empress passed by.

Presently, Eugénie had felt tired and sat down. She looked around and said, very quietly, but very sadly:

'All has changed and we also are much changed.'

And so, the Empress went on her way to Cap Martin, where she had built a villa which she named Cyrnos. She loved being there, surrounded by flowers of every hue and scent, beyond which lay the ripples of the silver-edged Mediterranean.

While the Empress is living quietly in her lovely villa let us relive the Paris of those days. London was interesting but Paris enthralling.

Paris has changed since the eighties and nineties; much more so than London.

In England, the tempo of life is slower, people remain satisfied with things as they find them, but in France, events outstrip ideas, sometimes for the better, but more often for the worse.

A well-known French doctor once told me that a medical man's life in England was far easier. There, the public are content to wait patiently for TIME to cure them; over here, they insist on being cured instantly, and so it goes with everything.

The charm of Paris lies in the many facets of its character.

Even today, in some quarters, one comes across a 'place' or 'impasse' paved with cobble stones, there are one or two tall shady trees, grey stone mansions covered with ivy, aged women sit gossiping on a bench in the shade, stray cats scavenge in the gutter; somewhere one can hear the high trill of a canary. There is a clatter of shoes, and the children come scurrying from school in their black alpaca aprons munching large *tartines* as they run. One senses the atmosphere of a provincial market town on the Loire; it seems so strange when one realizes that scarcely a mile away is the busy traffic and the plate glass windows of the ultramodern shops of the rue de la Paix.

In the eighties, there were no drains in Paris, and from time to time, the famous *vidangeurs* would appear. I used to enjoy watching them. They drove up in a huge covered cart and would carry to the different houses, long, rather wide, metal containers on their backs. They wore leather clothes with hooded caps on their heads, and looked most macabre.

They would enter the house by the *porte cochère*, where they went, I never knew, but they emerged later with the containers well screwed down, then off they drove to the next house.

As there were no bathrooms in those days, on special occasions when we wanted a bath, a message would be sent to the nearest *bains chauds*. Two men in blue linen blouses would arrive in a kind of cart with a copper contraption filled with steaming hot water.

First of all, the men dragged out a large and long white metal bath, and with much swearing and loud talking, would bring it up to the required room. Once installed there, on a square of rubber, they would line the bath with a kind of rough sheet, which went well over the sides. Satisfied that this was all in order, they would descend once more to fetch two buckets of boiling water which they carried suspended from a wooden yoke on their shoulders.

Then two packets of starch were thrown into the water – it was supposed to be soothing to the skin. I remember vividly, that the sheet scraped one's body and the men smelt of steam and starch.

We were generally ordered by the doctor to take a bath like this, after a contagious disease. How many more germs one caught, after such an immersion is another matter; but it was the custom: afterwards we were once more allowed to mix with our friends, as all danger was supposed to be over. I wonder?

The great joy of children, rich as well as poor, were the goats.

One could hear the tinkling of their little bells as they passed down the street, followed by a man generally from the mountains of Savoy, tall and thin with his béret at a rakish angle.

As he came along, playing his pipe, people ran to their doors with jugs and cans; then the man sat down on the kerb to milk the wretched animals. I think it cost two sous a jug.

The man did not wear overalls or wash his hands, but still we survived and enjoyed this drink which was supposed to cure consumption, or perhaps prevent it, I forget which.

It was all very colourful. Life was gay, but simple compared to now.

With the discovery of 'germs', living has become slightly tedious. One seems conscious of being alive, the fear of death walks with us all the time.

In those days, we feared nothing, germs might be lurking around, but as we had not made their acquaintance, we did not bother. All was so easy. We ate and drank anything we desired, never giving a thought to the consequences.

Men enjoyed life to the bitter end; women also. Children were never told that anything was bad for their health. Life may not have been so prolonged, but what did that matter? We must all die, but while we were alive, life was *insouciant*, full of light and gaiety, and not full of the everlasting anxiety to live longer.

There was always a little group of loiterers clustered at the bottom of the Champs-Élysées watching the 'omnibuses', lumbering kind of coaches, dragged from the *banlieus* by two miserable-looking horses. When they reached the beginning of the steep ascent from the Place de la Concorde to the Arc de Triomphe, there were men in blouses waiting with a spare horse, to be harnessed in front of the others, so that they might achieve the hope of the *cocher* that they would get to the top of the hill.

When, after much swearing and pulling, the sweating horses had dragged the clumsy vehicle to the summit, the spare horse was unhitched and led down to return with the next bus. What a life!

On a summer morning, people would take an open *fiacre* and drive down the boulevards, there to stop and buy *pommes de terre frites* from a man who had a little open booth where he fried furiously all day long. He would sprinkle some with salt, slip them into a bag and charge two sous. He had an enormous clientele. I believe he made quite a fortune in a few years.

Then there were the toy shops – no child now living can even dream what they contained.

The two principal ones were 'Le Nain bleu' and 'Aux Paradis des Enfants'.

There were dolls of all sizes and shapes, some life-size and made to the exact likeness of some special child, dressed with the greatest luxury from its head of real curly hair to its exquisite little buttoned boots; others made of wax, dressed in long clothes of real lace, even the nappies could be embroidered with coronet and initial of the purchaser. Then there were dolls' houses containing all one could imagine, down to the brooms, dusters, caps and aprons for the *bonne*.

For the boys, there were whole uniforms of almost every regiment, complete with sword or gun, rocking horses covered with real skin, and boxes of lead soldiers by the thousand. If modern children were taken there, they would remain with their mouths open in amazement and probably would have difficulty in ever shutting them again.

Mechanical toys were a great attraction, from performing animals to exquisite marquis and marquises dancing a minuet, golden feathered birds jumping from perch to perch and singing to their hearts' content, all so realistic.

Next to such shops might be a *charcuterie*, the *patronne* with dazzling white apron and long white sleeves would stand surrounded by boars' heads, hams, sausages of every shape and enticing-looking *pâtés*, and slices of pink *foix gras*; the whole shop scrupulously clean and every article laid out on marble slabs.

From the rue de Rivoli and the rue de la Paix one would saunter towards the Champs-Élysées which were full of *nounous* and children, all dressed in dazzling colours, it was like a kaleidoscope, the former suckling their charges quite oblivious of decency, their huge bosoms, filled with rich milk, exposed to the gaze of the passing crowds.

Sometimes oldish men would stop and relish the sight and the *nounou* would smile and make some simple remark: '*Vous en voudriez bien un peu, hein!*'

The *vieux marcheur* would answer: '*Je voudrais bien être le gosse*', and pass on smiling broadly.

Then there was the *marchand de coco*, carrying on his back a sort of pagoda, adorned with bells and flags, and covered with red cotton velvet. The man, dressed in a fantastic get-up, would jingle the bells to attract attention. The container had a little tap which he would turn and out flowed the coco, which was delicious, made of liquorice and sassifras. He poured it into small cups and we used to love it.

I wonder where he could have washed the cups, but again we knew nothing of germs and cared less; so why worry?

A little further on, at the 'Rond Point' stood a chef, in his immaculate white clothes and high hat, making *des gaufres* over a stove. They were a kind of waffle, slightly powdered with sugar and flavoured with real vanilla, which he had in long black sticks. What a heavenly taste they had!

Then perhaps a *marchand de plaisir* would pass along, calling: '*Allons, Mesdames, c'est le plaisir, le plaisir des dames.*'

He always wore a blue béret.

The *plaisirs* were in two shapes, one, a long cornet, the other, folded over like a small table napkin. They were made of a very brittle pastry resembling ice cream wafers, but much more exciting in taste and texture.

Nobody minded stopping to buy these; very smart victorias might draw up to the kerb, ladies would send their footman to call these men to the carriage, then they would drive away, eating the *plaisirs* quite openly.

In the early morning, the women cooks and chefs would go to market carrying large baskets. The milk was brought in open pails to the houses, all the rest the cook would purchase and bring back from the market.

The *boulangeries* were a dream, with the *pain de ménage*, long loaves which had holes in the *mie* and a slightly sour flavour; one cut them in slanting slices. Then the *flutes, croissants* and *petit pains* – *enfin* it really was bread in those days.

At the *patissiers, brioches, madeleines* and every imaginable kind of pastry and cake could be purchased. It was the fashionable thing to do after a morning walk in the Avenue de l'Impératrice, to enter Gagé, the *patissier* in the place de l'Étoile, eat a cake or one of their mayonnaise sandwiches, and drink a glass of Marsala, a sweet wine.

In the early hours of the morning when it was scarcely light, a very different kind of equipage drove up to these places. It was the covered cart of the *Petites Soeurs des Pauvres*, who would climb humbly down from their ramshackle vehicle dressed in well-worn habits, and enter the establishment to beg for the remains left behind by the disdainful ladies, who had, perhaps, nibbled some delicacy, and left the rest of it on the plate. These wonderful women would carry between them baskets; sometimes well filled, and at others half empty, but always grateful; with a prayer and a blessing they would continue their rounds until they returned to their convent where they sheltered and fed tiny babies, foundlings from the streets, and aged people; it was only after these were satisfied that they allowed themselves to eat what was left.

Fashions were changing rapidly, the bustles were already disappearing; Worth was transforming gowns into full tulle skirts, the bodice of satin ending in front in a point.

Opera cloaks were long and ample and of various materials, mostly of cloth trimmed with huge but soft sheepskin collars.

Every woman in Society had her ladies' maid, who spent the morning ironing each gown to be worn that day.

I remember a shop in the rue Auber belonging to an English firm, Kerby and Beard, which sold mostly hairpins, hatpins, in fact, pins of every size and shape. They must have made a fortune, as nobody of note bought these things anywhere else; only England was supposed to be capable of producing such a valuable addition to one's toilette.

Another shop supposed to be very smart, was near the Opera and was called 'Old England'. Every child who wore a sailor suit made by that shop was supposed to have the *chic Anglats*. When we were children, my brother and I were taken there for our clothes. I remember that they specialized in tartan kilts as well, but, of course, the French knew nothing of the Clan tartans, and went about wearing the tartans of all the families of Scotland from Royal Stuart, to the smallest sept.

Opposite was 'Boissier', the famous sweet shop. One used to stop here when on the way to the Opera or theatre to buy a blue carton of heavenly *petit fours* in which lay a minute pair of silvered tin sugar tongs, so as not to soil the long suede gloves. You would just lift one of these sweets with this instrument, and bite without touching the tongs, as only one pair was supplied for the use of the whole party.

Perhaps the greatest fascination of the people of France is their absolute independence of their neighbour's opinion – they are individuals above all.

Je m'en fiche (I don't care) might well be their motto.

When the time comes for eating, they sit down, tuck their napkins under their chins and cut huge pieces of bread with which to wipe their plates clean so as not to lose any of the exquisite food. Of course, this refers to the lower *bourgeoisie*, but in a different manner the upper classes are the same, it runs through the whole country. The clubman says: '*Je m'en fiche*', the lady of Society also, and they both mean it.

Au fond, it is a delicious feeling; there is nothing like it in England because obviously it is contrary to the British mentality. They are too anxious about what other people think. From babyhood, they are told 'be careful or the lady next door will hear you', and, above all, they are taught to restrain their feelings in public.

Frenchmen embrace when they meet or part, but in England if a mother kisses her son in front of his school friends, the whole family blushes at her abandoned behaviour, and the child is marked for life.

The French are born, live and die just naturally and yet they have given to the world its greatest actors and actresses.

The strongest contrast between the two cities was most noticeable on Sundays.

In London, Sunday was a day of gloom; nobody who was anybody, dared show their face, as it was not the thing to be seen in town during the week-end. All the world was supposed to be revelling in expensive tea-gowns, in luxurious country houses. So the blinds were discreetly lowered, and we were not even allowed to play the piano, lest someone passing along the other side of Grosvenor Square, might hear a note. Going to Mass at Farm Street at eleven o'clock, was all that we were permitted; my father in his top hat and frock coat; Mamma, being small, had almost to run to keep up with his long strides. We children, dressed up to kill, solemnly walked behind. As it was absolutely unheard of to have the horses out on Sunday, there was nothing else to do, but walk.

I shall always remember the silence of the empty streets, no carriages, no hansom cabs, no clatter of horses' hoofs – it was tragic.

Now, when we returned to my beloved Paris, how different it all was.

On our way to Mass at St. Philip du Roule, the city was full of life, *fiacres* and carriages dashing past; *blanchisseuses* in their muslin caps carrying home the linen in large covered baskets – they always did this on Sundays though I never knew why.

Usually we went to the twelve o'clock Low Mass, a short Mass, but often the music consisted of the organ, violins, harps, 'cello and some wonderful artiste from the Opera.

In the middle of all this, the *vieille chaisière*, an old woman in black with a black lace cap, would struggle and push her way through the rows of chairs, and mutter most evilly if you gave her 'one sou' instead of the regulation 'two sous', in fact, she would mutter and threaten, until you fumbled and found another coin to quiet her.

Then there were the two *quêtes*, or collections; the first, 'for the parish, please', was generally taken by a lady of some importance who was escorted by the Church *Suisse* arrayed in all the glory of his feathered cocked hat and frock coat, heavily embroidered with gold lace, red plush knee breeches and buckled shoes – he carried his long staff with a huge silver knob, truly a most imposing personage.

The second *quête*, 'for the poor, please', was taken up by a priest, who was escorted by a black-garbed *huissier* who wore a silver chain and heavy medallion and carried a short black rod with a silver knob. There was so much to see and hear, that there was little time left in which to pray.

Then we came out into the bright sunshine; all around were citizens dressed in their Sunday best, all talking vigorously as they went home to a delicious *déjeuner*, and afterwards to walk in the Avenue de l'Impératrice, or drive in an open carriage in the Bois de Boulogne.

If they hired a *fiacre*, the whole family crowded in, the *cocher* didn't seem to mind how many, perhaps the poor horse did, only he could not express his sentiments.

In the evening, there would be another huge repast, sometimes at home, but more often in a café where *père, mère, la tante* and both grandparents sat down with the children.

La mère suckled the baby when it howled, and if that did not suffice, she dipped a finger in a wine glass, and gave it to the baby to suck.

143

So there they sat, laughing and joking with their neighbours and friends as they passed and repassed along the boulevard.

In those days, it was a religion for the populace to be gay and light-hearted. They believed in their Church and went to Mass on Sundays and feast days; for the rest, their life was their own and no affair of *le bon Dieu*.

I wonder if *le bon Dieu* was of the same opinion?

During Lent, all Society functions ceased, and large congregations, mostly of women, filled the more fashionable churches like the Madeleine, St. Augustin's or Notre-Dame.

In all of these, famous preachers ascended the pulpit to thunder exhortations or denunciations twice a week.

These preachers were as famous in their own way as the actors of the Théâtre Français, their impassioned discourses were popular even with the frivolous *mondaines*. People fought and pushed to reach good places near the pulpit, the crowds were so great that they thronged the aisles and stood in every available spot, even sitting on the altar steps.

It was a solemn moment when, having knelt before the High Altar as if to implore divine inspiration, the preacher, often a Franciscan or Dominican monk, would come down preceded by the Sacristan who led him to the pulpit. The Curé, and other priests sat on wooden benches at the side of the High Altar.

When all were seated, the preacher having made the Sign of the Cross, began his sermon. Not a sound broke the silence, not even a stifled cough, one could feel the atmosphere tense with excitement.

Then came a torrent of words, fierce denunciations of the sins of Society and exhortations to repentance, all in polished but dramatic rhetoric, which stirred one's innermost soul.

When he finished there was almost a sigh of release.

Lent really meant a renunciation of pleasure in those days; some fasted but many abstained.

When Holy Week approached, my mother started worrying how we would live through Good Friday, as on that day no meat, milk, butter, eggs and, of course, no fats were allowed, so what would we eat?

When the day arrived, the chef would begin creating his marvellous dishes at the crack of dawn; by midday the table groaned under his *chef d'œuvres* and every conceivable delicacy lay before our eyes. The only thing I can remember is, that later in the day I groaned, but not from starvation as Mama had feared, but from indigestion.

On Holy Saturday, after midday, Easter eggs began to appear; eggs of all sizes, from tiny ones made of cardboard containing a minute yellow chick, to huge cartons made to hold an almost life-size doll with all its trousseau.

Flowers poured into the house from all our friends, then on Easter Sunday everybody wore something new just for luck.

15 IMPERIAL ECHOES

In 1892, I married and from a state of never being allowed out of the *porte cochère* by myself, I was able to feel as I walked down the rue de Logelbach where my husband, Sasha, and I were living, at any moment I might be kidnapped by a passing man, indeed; I was somewhat disappointed that it did not happen.

From the hour of my marriage, life became a beautiful dream.

Everything was now permitted. Restaurants, immoral plays, flirtations, and I became acquainted with all the *piquante* scandals of the hour.

One of the very first in which, in a way, I became involved happened like this.

It was a sad episode. I wonder if I can employ that word – an episode in two lives, perhaps, but a tragedy in the third.

The man was a friend of mine. I will call him Comte de Boisdechêne; those who remember the story may recognize him. He was a widower with an only son who was still very young, in fact only eighteen years old. To me, the Comte seemed an old man; actually he was about sixty, tall, with a graceful figure, good looking, hair just turning grey at the temples, a small pointed beard, exquisite hands, exquisitely kept. I remember his rings, a Cabochon sapphire and a Cabochon ruby; he also wore a bangle, so many men did in those days. He was cultured, had great charm, was a good conversationalist and knew well how to capture the woman who attracted him at the moment.

He was very wealthy, but alas he was sixty – to me, that seemed beyond the grave. I used to meet him often, as although he was years older than either Sasha or I, we had become great friends. I amused him and Sasha interested him.

One day, he invited us to luncheon at his lovely home on the other side of the river. All that one could dream of seemed to exist in that house.

During *déjeuner*, when we were alone with him, he began:

'*Mes chers petits amis*, I have asked you to come today to partake of my joy. I am engaged!'

I had a shock, he had become a kind of *amitié amoureux* to me; I fancied he was rather in love with me. However, at that time, I always imagined this of every man I met.

He continued:

'A few weeks ago, I spent some days with old friends in the Ardennes. They told me of their granddaughter Marie-Amélie, who was just eighteen – your own age,' he said turning to me. I was going to speak, but he stopped me and went on:

'She was leaving the convent school and they imagined that she knew nothing of life. She arrived. I lost my head and my heart. It took only a few days for me to convince her that I was the only man in the world, indeed she had seen no other. Have I been foolish or have I been wise? *Quien sabe!* time will show. I know I shall be called by every name under the sun. I am completely in her power. I never thought that *l'Amour* in any tongue sung, recited or prayed for could amount to what I feel. Here is Marie-Amélie.' At this he produced from his pocket a miniature, a veritable dream – nothing can describe that face, that look, that hair. I just gasped, then Sasha said rather solemnly:

'Are you sure of her?'

'*Mon cher*, how can one know of a certainty,' said Philippe.

'Does your son André know?'

'My son is in Morocco.' That closed the discussion.

A month later we were again asked to luncheon. Sasha and I rather dreaded meeting La Comtesse de Boisdechêne. Would we be disappointed? Miniatures often lie!

As we entered the house, my friend flew down to meet us, flushed with excitement.

'*Venez, mes amis.* You are the first to meet the most adorable woman in the world.'

The drawing-room door was thrown open by a footman and I saw before me a figure, slender and willowy, really a lovely child with large blue eyes, still unawakened to life. She curtseyed as very young women still do in France to older ladies. I had time to look at her. She was not only beautiful but ethereal. Dressed in the thinnest of white muslin, her waist girdled by a wide red sash; on one side of her skirt, a bunch of cherries, round her slender neck a narrow red velvet ribbon.

She looked exactly like a Madonna of the Italian school – the perfect oval of her face, her sapphire-blue eyes, and her jet-black lustrous hair completed a remarkable picture. Perhaps the reader may think this an exaggerated description, but it is not.

She seemed so natural as she said:

'We must be friends.'

We were the same age, and she knew nobody, as yet. Philippe only had eyes for her, and no wonder.

Whilst Sasha was talking to Marie-Amélie, Philippe drew me aside, and whispered:

'*Eh bien?*'

What could I reply but: 'She is more lovely than I imagined her.'

'Tell me the truth. Do I look like her husband?'

I laughed. 'You must know better than anybody.'

He persisted: 'You know what I am asking?'

'Then you want my true opinion?'

'Yes.'

'*Alors mon ami!* You have a child instead of a wife...'

They went to Italy to prolong their honeymoon, and we had word of them from Naples: then we left for England, it was months before we returned to Paris.

How I hated those journeys! but we never left for the coast before wiring to the harbour master, to ask how the sea was looking, pretending that we had with us a very delicate invalid. Often all was ready, everything packed, and the reply would be 'rough', then, all would be postponed. How spoilt I was in those days.

When we returned to Paris, Sasha went to see Philippe, who told him that his wife had just gone out with André, his son, who had returned from Morocco, and he seemed very pleased that they were such friends.

Later, I saw her at parties. She had become still more beautiful, the *ingénue* had given place to a most perfect *femme du monde*. She was ablaze with jewels, her gowns the latest from Worth; she was attractive beyond words.

Philippe followed her with adoring eyes, but at once I guessed the truth, the eyes of his son André, followed her still more closely. To the world it seemed quite natural, stepmother and stepson.

After a time, I believe Philippe noticed it, but I was not quite sure until one day a note arrived from him, asking me to receive him alone at seven o'clock that evening.

He came, he seemed strangely taut, and for a time we spoke of trifles.

Then I said:

'Philippe, it is not for words like these that you have come.'

'*Ma chère petite amie*, it is to ask your help. Marie-Amélie and André are in love!'

'Are you sure?'

'I am sure! For some time I have sensed, but tried to ignore it. Now, the possibility of doing so has vanished. Last night we went to a party at the Austrian Embassy. Marie-Amélie looked so lovely that I felt afraid of such beauty. We came home later. As you know, we have separate rooms. I kissed her good night; she seemed more tender to me than ever. Was it remorse? I wonder?

'Much later, I longed for her, if only just a peep at her perfection.

'HER room was empty. I could not understand it. Then a horrid fear of learning the truth shook me, but at the same time a demon of curiosity took possession of my soul. I went softly upstairs to André's *appartement*.

'I listened! Nothing!

'Still as in a trance, I crept into his study, not a sound. I turned the handle of the door. HIS room was empty, the bed untouched.

'I felt cold, clammy. Where were they?

'By now, I had no doubt that they were together. Like a thief in my own house I walked down the stairs. I visited every room.

'Then I recalled a little boudoir, rarely used, except as a *vestiaire*. It was a pretty room, and I remembered that quite recently Marie-Amélie had chosen charming Louis XVI material, for the walls and curtains.

'I had asked her why, and she replied that it was nice for women to arrange themselves in attractive surroundings; so she had ordered sofas and chairs of the same period.

'Still walking as though in a dream, I turned the knob – the door was locked.

'Scarcely knowing what I did, I cried:

149

' *"Ouvrez au nom de la loi."*

'André must have thought it was the police. The key was turned, and the door opened.

'I stood looking in. There was no longer any doubt. Marie-Amélie stood perfectly still, but André came furiously towards me.

' "You have no right here," he cried, "this woman who was your wife, in name only, is my mistress!"

'Even at such a moment, *ma chère petite amie*, I realized the truth "they are young!"

'I closed the door and left them.

'I blame myself bitterly, I never made her my wife.'

'What do you mean?' I exclaimed.

'I was bewitched and feared to mar the perfect beauty of her body. She knew nothing of life, and seemed to be content with what I gave her.'

Here I interrupted him:

'Yes! until she met someone who gave her, what you in your selfishness refused.'

'*Alors! Quoi!*'

'There is only one way. Return home, call Marie-Amélie, take her in your arms: after all, in her eyes now, you are only her father.'

Philippe was not in a state to understand. He took up his hat and walked out of the room.

On the table, he left an envelope which doubtless he had intended to show me. In it was a note in Andre's handwriting, which explained all.

> *Mademoiselle ma mère.*
> I shall love you all my life.
> Your son and lover,
> ANDRÉ

A few days later, Philippe came to me once more. He seemed so changed, so much older. As he kissed my hand, he said:

'I have come to say *adieu*.'

'Where are you going,' I cried.

'That is my secret. I go to expiate my crime. Say good-bye to Sasha, and never mention this visit to anyone.'

So Philippe left, never to re-enter the lives of those who had known him.

André went to Morocco. Marie-Amélie lived on in that wonderful house, at first dressed in deep mourning but only for a time; later from black to mauve, then every hue under the sun was her life.

Although more than twenty years had passed since the debacle I frequently met those who delighted to recall intimate pictures of Eugénie in her glory.

One evening, I was dining with Comtesse Robert de Fitz-James, in her lovely *appartement* in the rue de Constantine.

It was a large party, one of those endless dinners, which in those days seemed quite natural; one was invited to eat the best of everything. For days before, the chef and his aides had been working on these marvellous creations. Before deciding on a new chef, the great thing was to try him out on two dishes, spinach and soufflé. If he passed muster in these he was engaged as all the rest would be easy.

At Rosa de Fitz-James's, the great *spécialité* was cold chicken. The chickens were fed for weeks before they were allowed to grace her table. When these wonderful fowl were brought in, they were usually so heavy that one man had difficulty in passing them round. People's mouths watered.

The chef never allowed them to grow quite cold so as to become too stiff, but only just cold enough to be called *poulets froids* but, enough of this, let us return to that evening.

Next to me at table sat Amiral Duperré. He and Charles de Fitz-James had served together in the Navy. He was one of the favourites of the Imperial Court of the Second Empire.

Amiral Duperré had retained the magnetic charm of that time, his whole personality seemed reminiscent of the sailor and *grand seigneur*.

He turned to me, saying:

'*Ma chère enfant*, what a pity you were born too late, that you never knew the life so elegant, so amorous, of the Imperial Court. With your character and your love of gaiety, you would have taken part in all the glitter which shone around the Empress. *Ah! comme c'était beau!*'

151

'*Cher amiral,* as I was born too late and I shall never see it, could you not revive some scenes before my eyes. You that have known it all so intimately? Let us leave the present and fly back to when the Tuileries were alive and you and my brother-in-law, Charles de Fitz-James, were breaking hearts, perhaps paining your own for a while now and then!'

'Would it really amuse you?' he asked.

So, after dinner, when all were talking and admiring for the hundredth time, the pictures and works of art those lovely rooms contained, the old man took me to a boudoir, where we sat together surrounded by the Fitz-James's ancestors, who looked down on us from the walls, Louis XVI furniture, gold snuff boxes, ormulu clocks and priceless but quite useless knick-knacks, which cost a fortune.

There were only one or two lamps alight, and the shadows allowed one's visions to become realistic as he spoke.

'Where shall I begin?' He took my hand and gently kissed it, we were quite alone. From the vista of rooms came the hum of voices, but nobody came near us; the flowers seemed to bend their slender heads as though to listen. The only sound was when a petal fell on the thick carpet. I wondered when he would commence, he was so silent.

Then he began:

'We were at Compiègne, we used to be invited for weeks at a time. Guests came and went, but somehow Charles de Fitz-James, Poché as he was nicknamed, and myself were always there.

'I suppose we were gay and rather "devil may care"; this pleased the Empress.

'It was a pleasant life, we were free to go to Paris whenever we liked. Naturally we had our naval duties, but I am speaking of when we were on leave.

'How lovely those women were! and how reckless: the Empress seemed a being quite apart.

'One evening stands out above all. It was in November. I do not know the reason, as so many must have resembled it, but I have never forgotten this particular scene.

'We were in the music room, the curtains were drawn, as the short day had closed in, many lamps with their elaborate frilled shades were lighted. The Gobelins tapestry covering the walls seemed to come to life.

'The chandeliers had not been lit so the painted ceiling could scarcely be discerned.

'All the brightness reflected from those lamps shone on the occupants of this beautiful room.

'The large tea-table laden with silver and priceless china stood alone in a far corner, we had sat around it, but now the chairs looked lonely and in disorder. The Empress reclined gracefully in a large arm-chair, her lovely head resting on one hand, her arm showing its beauty as the wide sleeve had fallen back – her arms and hands were so perfect. Her hair fell in red golden ringlets on her shoulders, her eyes like two blue stars with a tinge of sadness, seemed to flood the whole room with a mixture of fear, pain and laughter.

'Gounod was seated at the piano, playing one of his most recent compositions.

'Perhaps, *mon enfant*, you will think that I am romancing, but I assure you that it all stands out in my mind as clearly as a Winterhalter picture.

'That day the Empress wore on her perfect body a robe of white tulle, a sash of black velvet hung in long loops at her side, a red rose nestled in her auburn hair and a tiny foot shod in a black satin slipper peeped from beneath the huge crinoline. I could not take my eyes from such grace and perfection.

'Mélanie de Pourtalès sat a little away. She, I remember, was in blue, the colour which matched her eyes. Charles de Fitz-James was leaning on the back of her chair, he was rarely further away.

'Pauline de Metternich, whilst seemingly listening, was repeating in her mind the rôle that she would act that evening.

'Madame Lebreton sat slightly in the background. She was reader to the Empress and it made just a little difference. Czartoriski, Merimée and Pasteur completed the *ensemble*.

'I stood in a far corner seeing and yet unseen as I studied each person. Were they enjoying the music which was so beautiful, or were they far away in their thoughts? I took a pencil and piece of paper and as my eyes passed from one to the other I wrote. I found the scrap of paper a few days ago and this is what I had written.

The Empress is far away in her thoughts, perhaps a little jealous – where is her husband? She does not really care now, but still it is a tiresome feeling to think that he is just killing himself. It is humiliating, after all, not one of those women with whom he amuses himself is nearly as beautiful or clever or attractive as I – Then Louis (her son), is not strong and seems to lack ambition – *au fond c'est très difficile*. Will Worth, I wonder, send my new gown in time for me to wear it tonight?

Mélanie is lovely and so much younger than I am – it must be amusing to be able to have a 'Charles' at one's side – how beautifully Gounod is playing. 'Bravo! bravo! Monsieur Gounod, *c'est admirable*.'

Mélanie in her blue gown is trying to concentrate on the divine music but Charles de Fitz-James is just *effleurant* her shoulder whispering softly, but she thinks: 'I must look lovely tonight in my gauze gown – will it be too transparent?'

Pauline is too busy to listen. She is organizing the tableaux and play for the evening, so many people will be there. She wonders if her gown will be as beautiful as she wants it to be.

'At this moment, the door opened softly, and the Emperor, putting his finger to his lips, and making a sign that no one should rise, walked in.

'Notwithstanding his gesture, all rose. Monsieur Gounod ceased playing – the charm was broken. . . .'

The Amiral stopped, Rosa came in and in her rather squeaky voice exclaimed:

'Really this is enough, all have left and I want to go to bed.'

Suddenly I was brought back with a jerk to the ancestors on the wall, the gold snuff boxes and my long drive to the rue de Logelback.

I realized as I saw more of Society, that wit perhaps counted more than any virtue, whatever form it took, whether cruel or caustic, kind or amusing.

One of the wittiest hostesses of this epoch was Comtesse Vera de Talleyrand, a Russian by birth and somewhat plain. She spoke French with a slight Slav accent which was rather attractive. Monsieur André de Fouquières, in his delightful memoirs, relates that one day Prince Troubetskoi asked her for a definition of life. Vera Talleyrand sighed and replied:

'One passes one's life saying farewell to those who leave until the day comes when you say farewell to those who stay.'

In the rue Tronchet, Mélanie de Pourtalès still held her Court. Her *salon* was adorned with *objets d'art*, pictures, sculpture and vitrines filled with lovely figurines, bronzes and crystal; she in the midst receiving all who counted in the world of those days.

There is a charming story told of her. Once, when she was visiting a famous and historic château, the old Curé of the village was amongst the guests at luncheon. When he was presented to her, he remarked:

'How honoured I feel to meet the beautiful Comtesse de Pourtalès.'

Turning to him, she said:

'Oh *mon Père*, if you had only seen me forty years ago, you would have realized that le Bon Dieu had created a work of art.'

This reminds me of the witty and pious Abbé Mugnier. He was very *mondain* and yet always retained a certain simplicity.

At a dinner party, the ladies were discussing 'faith'. One turned to the Abbé and said:

'Monsieur l'Abbé! you cannot really believe in hell?'

He hesitated a second, then with his benevolent smile replied:

'Madame, the belief in hell is a dogma of the Church. I do indeed believe in it, but I feel sure that it is empty!'

On another occasion, the Abbé was sitting at luncheon next to a very pretty woman, when one of the men of the party called out across the table:

'I'm sure, Monsieur l'Abbé, you would refuse to kiss your charming neighbour.'

'Certainly,' he replied 'since my neighbour is not yet a relic.'

16 ENTER 'MAXIMS'

The extraordinary popularity of Albert Edward, Prince of Wales, dated from the time when in his early teens he accompanied his parents on their visit to Napoleon III and the Empress Eugénie. When he returned as a young man, he gained a place in the heart of every French man and woman, a place which no political intrigue could affect; they looked upon him almost as one of themselves.

Many times there was tension between the French and British Governments, but it never touched his popularity. The French regarded him as a being apart – something which belonged to them. He had only to appear in some new style of apparel, and the very next day, people of every class would murmur:

'*Le Prince porte telle ou telle nouveauté* and every shop from the rue de la Paix to the Temple would display an imitation, good or bad, of his attire.

His picture was in every window, his effigy was printed or woven on ladies' shawls, glove boxes, handkerchief sachets – on fans and even cakes of soap.

Monarchs and Princes would visit the capital, but none could rouse the spirit of France, as he was able to do.

They were so genuinely fond of him, that often in a crowded place they would respect his incognito; no other prince ever became so much a part of themselves, as Albert Edward, Prince of Wales.

Maxims was just beginning its long and successful career. When I was supping there many years later, it was considered very *risqué* for a young woman to be seen there, and yet every night there were many trying their wings in this establishment. I sat next to a man, no longer young, who knew Paris *au fond*. He told me of the origin of this famous restaurant.

'I wonder if the Prince would be interested,' he said, pointing to the Prince of Wales. Then, without further ado, he left me and went across to where the Royal party was supping.

On his return he told me the story. Maxim was an obscure

waiter who saved a few hundred francs and bought a small café, which had been more or less destroyed by the mob during the Franco-Prussian war, when an Italian ice-cream merchant who owned it at the time, had hoisted a German flag.

When young Maxim first opened, the *cochers de fiacres* were his only clients; at length he failed and it was bought by a man named Benoit, who had plenty of capital, and was able to engage a first-class chef, then he managed to get hold of Cornuchet, who later became Monsieur Cornuchet de Deauville, the founder of that resort.

Cornuchet was then *maître d'hôtel* at Durands, the famous restaurant. Between them Maxims rose to fame, but I think it was really *lancé* by Max Lebaudy, the fantastic millionaire. From that time Maxims never looked back.

Monarchs, Grand Dukes, *demi-mondaines*, rich Americans and all who were bent on 'seeing life' went there, and so it is even today. Maxims for them means excitement, perdition, sin, and a longing to taste all they imagine it contains.

Although France had forgotten the time of the Empire, and few were left who remembered it, it was always a point of discussion, when the Empress Eugénie arrived in Paris, and stayed at the Hôtel Continental. Even people who had not had the honour of having been presented to her, would feel just a little shocked and wonder if she was heartless.

How could she look on that garden, and the stones of the ruined palace, which were still to be seen strewn about in burnt heaps?

I remember once at a luncheon party given by the Grand Duchesse Vladimir, someone mentioned that the Empress had arrived at the Continental. The usual remarks flew around, she had no feelings or sentiment; how could she, year after year, choose just this view, where her husband and son had walked in all their glory, and which, later, she had to abandon, the mob shouting 'Death to the Spaniard' in her ears?

Then an old man, I still see him with his white pointed beard, waited until the recriminations were slowing down, and in a quiet tone, he said:

'*Mesdames et Messieurs*, every head is a world of its own, to which no one else is admitted, so do not let us judge a matter of which we know nothing. Let us keep our own in order lest somebody might discover what it contains.'

All laughed, but his words remained as a rebuke.

An old courtier of the Empire told me of a scene of unsurpassed beauty which he witnessed when the Court resided at Biarritz.

It took place in September 1858. I will relate it as he described it to me one evening as we walked on the terrace of the Villa St. Priest in Cannes:

'Life in Biarritz was fantastic. The Empress loved this little fishing village. She felt free, meeting just the people she and the Emperor fancied, and above all, it was so near to Spain.

'Each day brought a fresh idea, yachting, walking or driving. We would start early and often not return until two o'clock the next morning.

'Tonight, the air is so soft and the sea so still that I am reminded of another such evening long, long ago, when we were all so full of life, craving for excitement, never tired and ever ready to follow the least wish of the Empress.

'Eugénie was ever beautiful, but no one who has not seen her at the moment when she entered a *salon* filled with guests, can have any idea of her truly ethereal beauty. She would stand there with an expression of kindness and benevolence.

'She knew so well how to address each person with the very phrase that would enchant, her eyes seemed to seek the one to whom she spoke. It was impossible not to love her. In private, she was free in her speech, talking much, asking and answering questions, very sure of her opinion, but usually those opinions were based on kindness and generosity.

'The day to which I now allude, we started from the Villa Eugénie, a party of about thirty people in two charabancs. The servants followed in an omnibus, with all the necessities for our different repasts. The carriages were drawn by four horses, and we simply flew along. Our route was, to say the least, slightly dangerous, as we zigzagged the narrow roads, crossing bridges which seemed hardly strong enough to sustain a wheelbarrow.

'Eventually we stopped, and mounted mules led by Spanish

muleteers, who took us to our destination, an enormous cave used by the smugglers of contraband goods.

'While we visited the Grotto, the Spaniards climbed on to the top of the rocks and sang, accompanying themselves on guitars. Torches were lighted to guide us into the depths of the cave; the whole scene was weird and macabre, but grand.

'When evening drew nigh, a table stood on the grass laid ready for dinner.

'We sat down, a happy party, laughing, talking, singing snatches of the peasants' songs. We were rejoicing to see the gaiety and happiness of the Empress. She seemed to revive on breathing the soft air of Spain which lay so near.

'During the dinner, the muleteers never ceased to play and sing, with the gaiety and pathos, mingled with the graceful charm of Spain.

'As the evening proceeded, Eugénie's emotion was visible, and yet controlled. It was the emotion of one who had regained the country of her birth; all seemed to experience this feeling in unison with Her Majesty.

'The atmosphere was so perfect, the surroundings so barren and wild, not the slightest breeze even ruffled the ladies' fichus. Nothing stirred, nothing moved. The smoke from our cigars lingered as if loath to leave the earth.

'A large space had been cleared before us. The servants had retired to their dinner.

'Presently, the muleteers came into the circle, and began to dance to the sound of their guitars.

'The Empress sat there, a rapt expression on her face. Suddenly she rose from her chair, she seemed to hesitate, then, throwing aside her hat and cloak, she joined them and danced a fandango so gracefully, so simply, her face expressing the joy she was feeling at being able to convey in every movement, her love for Spain, which she could so rarely show.'

My friend, overcome with the emotion which he had evoked, paused a while, and then he said to me:

'That picture I have ever carried in my head. I was in love with Eugénie, but it was a love of devotion, of respect, of abnegation. Do you understand, *ma petite*, the meaning of that word?'

The last ten years of the nineteenth century were so vivid, and full of splendour that the earlier decades were but shadows of their brilliance. Royalties and Commoners alike lived their lives to the full, and sought to extract the uttermost from each successive hour, every second which was not filled with excitement was considered a second lost.

Paris vibrated to the sound of music, love, laughter, and folly, people danced the hours away. Often disaster followed close behind, but what did that matter; life was meant to be lived for the moment, tragedies might come in the future, but whilst the present lasted it was divine.

All the *grand monde* feasted and spent fortunes; they were delighted, the French were enchanted, so why regret?

The Prince of Wales was the leader of this joyous band, then came the Russian Grand Dukes, Vladimir, Alexis and Paul.

The Grand Duke Vladimir was Imperial in every feature, his deep voice seemed to shake the very walls when he entered one of the celebrated restaurants.

The Grand Duke Alexis was undoubtedly the handsomest, a giant in stature, fair haired, his beard almost the colour of gold – he had a most imposing personality and possessed great charm. His intimate friend was Madame Ballata; in fact he was rarely seen without her by his side. He was lavish in his generosity and well known as being a part of that Paris *qui s'amuse*.

He died comparatively young, Paris mourned him as if he had indeed been her own. I remember his funeral took place with full military honours, a truly remarkable tribute to a foreigner.

My husband was one of the officials who had to follow the coffin, carrying the Grand Duke's decorations on a cushion.

It was a long walk from the Russian Church in the rue Daru near the Arc de Triomphe to the Gare du Nord, where the body was placed on a train en route for St. Petersbourg for the burial.

It was summer time, and as far as I can remember, Sasha felt hot, and wanted to wipe the perspiration from his brow, quite forgetting that every eye was upon him.

He tried to reach his handkerchief, which is not easy when one is in uniform. Quite forgetting the decorations lying on the cushion, he held it by one corner and the precious medals and orders hung precariously in the air.

However, someone reminded him, and he hastily grasped that red and gold cushion as if he was balancing eggs upon it.

The Grand Duke Paul was a widower at this time – he remarried later. All three were the brothers of the Emperor Alexander III. When they appeared in a theatre or restaurant, people unconsciously stared in sheer admiration at their magnificent appearance. They were so sure of their own importance that they never hesitated to do anything they fancied.

These three, with the Prince of Wales, were the most colourful personalities of that time. Of the other monarchs who visited the Capital, King George I of Greece was the most respected.

Kings and Princes vied with each other in visiting this enchanting city; there never seemed to be a single week during which one or another was not arriving or departing. Here they found they were able to cast care aside, forget State matters and Imperial duties, and plunge into the vortex of pleasure that Paris alone can provide, for those who can afford to pay the price.

Ladies of Society and women of the *demi-monde* strained every nerve to catch their eye, or to attract their attention, if but for a fleeting moment.

Fêtes of unsurpassed splendour were organized for their pleasure, but these Royal and Imperial personages preferred *cabinets particuliers*, witty and attractive women, not of the *grand monde*.

The Jockey Club in Paris has always been one of the most exclusive clubs in Europe. My brother-in-law, Charles de Fitz-James, and his brother, the Duc de Fitz-James, were its leading spirits.

They were not always liked, as their wit was feared, especially Charles whose wit was proverbial. He was brilliant, sometimes even caustic but never brutal. His victims often joined in the laugh at their own expense, even if at times they resented the ridicule which touched them like the point of a rapier.

The club cabs were a great feature in Paris life; to be seen in a blue-lined coupé belonging to the 'Jockey' was the very 'chicest' thing.

As there were no telephones in those days, one sent a footman to ascertain if a cab was available for a certain day. If fortunate enough to secure one, a little brougham, with blue liveried coachman and smart well-groomed horse, would drive up at the appointed hour.

They always smelt of leather and frowstiness because most people drove for hours, and never thought of lowering the window, but although they were also rather expensive to hire, the very thought of being able to use one of these club cabs was sufficient pleasure to banish all thought of the cost.

About this time, there arrived from England, a most lovely girl. Almost at once, she was engaged by one of the leading dressmakers as a mannequin.

She created a furore, men suddenly began to encourage their wives to order new gowns.

Demi-mondaines were ordered by their lovers to buy new trousseaux, men seized any excuse to visit the establishment to gain a glimpse of this extraordinary beauty.

Her name was Nelly.

All this mad admiration did not affect her. She remained chaste, and eventually became engaged to a young man who worshipped her. He had quite a good position, but it was as nothing to the heights that she might have attained, The *grand couturier* for whom she worked simply coined money, orders rained down from every side.

Towards the end of the season, the young man asked Nelly to drive with him to Bougival, near Paris, where people go to lunch or dine, so that he might row her on the river. Her employer, hearing of the projected excursion, insisted that she should wear one of his prettiest models, also a hat of the latest fashion, not forgetting a parasol to match. Looking more lovely than ever, Nelly went off with her fiancé; after an excellent lunch, he hired a boat and they floated down the Seine.

Suddenly, for fun, she dipped the open parasol into the water, the skiff turned over; in a few seconds nothing was to be seen but the upturned boat and the floating umbrella.

The news spread like wildfire. 'Nelly is drowned.'

After her body was recovered, the head of Nelly's firm, absolutely wild with grief, declared that he was determined to give her a first-class funeral. This cost about 10,000 francs in those days.

So it took place, and hundreds of men followed the coffin with bared heads. Only in France could such a scene take place. I cannot see any other country thus honouring beauty in death.

In the year 1890, the phrase *fin de siècle* leaped into vogue; henceforth, everything was thus named. Any scandal, and there were many, was alluded to as really *fin de siècle*. As if such things had not existed before, even from the very beginning of time.

It became the fashion at this period for women of Society, and even those of the *demi-monde* to have their *parfumeur* blend them a special scent, suggestive of their personality. Such perfumes were jealously reserved as unique, so that none others might use them.

All this sounds very delightful, but all the same, it had its dangers.

A certain Comtesse de B. had a most devoted *amant*, who had been faithful to her for years and who thought that she was equally attracted to him. One morning, happening to visit the *garçonnière* of one of his greatest friends, he became conscious of an odour which seemed to be curiously familiar, but for the life of him he could not recall where it had last attracted his attention.

At the time, he said nothing, but that evening, sitting behind the Comtesse de B. in her box at the Opera, he sniffed the same subtle perfume, which had pervaded his friend's bachelor *appartement*.

During the *entr'acte* having nursed his wrath, he casually asked the Comtesse if she had seen their mutual friend the bachelor lately. With a detached air, she replied, that she had not seen him for months. Then he leant forward, and sniffed the air around her. Suddenly a fear assailed her. Could he possibly know anything? Her doubts were settled when her *amant* replied:

'Well, if you haven't met him, he must have met you!'

That night, she was more tender to him than ever, but even at the most blissful moment, a certain doubt lingered in his mind.

Another story of a similar type amuses me every time I recall it.

A certain Marquise de C. had spent a small fortune to obtain a particularly charming and exclusive model to wear at the reception to be given at the Russian Embassy, on the occasion of the State visit of the Emperor and Empress.

The evening came and she drove in her carriage to the reception.

As she alighted and turned to enter the vestibule, to her amazement and indignation, she saw a woman, whom she hated like poison, standing at the foot of the grand staircase dressed in a gown identical in every detail to the one she was wearing.

Trembling with rage, but quite undefeated, she drew her cloak closely around her, turned to her footman and ordered him to return to the house, and bring her maid with needles and sewing materials, as quickly as possible.

Meanwhile, she calmly walked to the cloakroom and occupied herself with rearranging her tiara. When the maid arrived, she joined her mistress, and they set to work.

Ripping the lace and chiffon from the lining of her evening cloak, they pinned the lace in cascades of jabots down the front of the gown, thus absolutely changing the whole design.

Then seizing some violets from a bowl on the table, they made them into tiny bunches which they fastened amongst the flounces of the skirt.

A quick glance into the mirror convinced the Marquise that all was well, she too ascended the stairs to enter the *salon*, conscious that the gown she wore was still unique.

In this last decade of the century, exactly thirty years after the death of Merimée, the thoughts of the Empress Eugénie seemed to return to him. At the time she was living in her villa at Cap Martin. Situated amidst the pines, it looked so white except for the flowers which almost smothered its façade.

The drawing-room on the ground floor opened on the spacious terrace, from which the whole panorama of that fantastic coast-line could be seen.

The Empress had often thought of Merimée, but it would be an ordeal to visit his tomb, yet she owed him so much.

He had always been faithful to her. The idea had long worried her, so she decided to drive to Cannes in her carriage with her nephew, Comte Primoli.

Her pilgrimage completed, she felt tired; perhaps the emotion had been too great. She drove to the Villa Kazbeck, belonging to the Grand Duke Michael of Russia, to lunch with her host and his wife, Comtesse Torby.

A little later, she was walking across the large ornate drawing-room, towards one of the open windows from which the almost eternally peaceful blue sea, and the surrounding Esterels could be seen, the roses seemed to be literally tumbling over each other.

A young boy, slender and fair, with blue eyes and exquisite hands and feet stood gazing out. He seemed to be dreaming, but as Her Majesty drew near, he turned and bowed very low.

The Empress appeared to be startled. She paused a moment, then she sat down and drew him towards her. He knelt by her side. Eugénie gently put her arm round him, saying:

'My dear little cousin, seeing you, has brought back a flood of memories, you are so like your father, he was one of my best friends, you have his hands,' she looked down, 'and also his lovely feet, you are truly the son of Charles de Fitz-James.'

It was a pathetic scene, the very young boy and the very old lady.

'So Your Majesty knew my father and my mother? Alas! I was very young when they died.'

'Yes,' said the Empress, 'I knew them well. Your father was one of the great lights of our Court. He married late in life. Your mother was so young and pretty – you have something of both.'

Saying this, she rose and said:

'My little cousin, do not forget an old woman of eighty who today has regained for a brief moment her youth on seeing the son of "Poché".'

During her long visits to the South of France, the Empress received and enjoyed the company of intellectual personalities.

In a book written by Monsieur Palaeologue, the distinguished diplomat, he recounts his conversations with Eugénie. The Duke of Alba in a conference to the Institut Français de Madrid, quotes from one of these delightful interviews.

'Madame,' asked Monsieur Palaeologue, 'knowing as you did, the situation in France and the hopes that were based on the restoration of the Empire, why did you allow the Prince Imperial to expose himself to the dangers of war?'

The Empress replied:

'How could I prevent him? He carried in his veins the blood of the Bonapartes inherited from his father and from me the sentiments of Don Quixote.'

Frequent visitors to her Villa Cyrnos were Monsieur Hanotaux, the eminent academician, Amiral Duperré and her close friends Mesdames de Gallifet, Sagan and Pourtalès, the latter had a luxurious residence in Cannes, the Villa St. Priest. One evening she asked me to go to see her. When I arrived, I was told that she had not yet returned, she had gone to luncheon with the Empress. So I waited; when she came in she said:

'*Ma petite*, forgive me but I have relived a part of my life today and that is why I am late. I will tell you about it, it will amuse you,' and as Mélanie, then years older than myself, sat with me in her drawing-room filled with flowers, this is what she told me:

'The Empress is eternal, her lovely profile, her eyes with that strange dark line beneath them, above all, that spirit, which is as alert as it was on that first day when I mounted the grand staircase of the Tuileries and rather trembled as Madame de Gallifet pronounced my name to Her Majesty.

'Today after *déjeuner*, she and I sat on the terrace, with all the blue of the Mediterranean before our eyes, and the pink hues of the roses around us: quietly the Empress passed her hand over her eyes and said:

' "I want to gaze and drink in this view, as I feel it will gradually fade from my vision. *Après ma chère amie*, even if night comes to me, you I hope, will ever be able to recall the scenes we have witnessed together. Some were very gay, others, well! let us bury those for the moment and enjoy the gay ones. Sadness is too easily with us.

' "Do you remember the day Charles de Fitz-James (Poché) arrived dressed as a highwayman with a mask and threatening us with pistols. You, I, and Madame de Morny were playing patience in the gardens of St. Cloud. How terrified we were when he demanded all our jewels, and after we had given him everything, he told us to undress and we were preparing to do so when you gave a scream and cried: 'It is this fool of a Poché!' You had recognized a mole on his chest, which he had bared to frighten us more. Of course, *ma chère*, you recognized it quite naturally; then all the trouble we had to get him away before the *gardes* heard the noise.

' "We hid him beneath one of our crinolines, yours I think! Naughty! anyhow the situation was saved."

'And so, *ma petite*, the Empress and I went from one amusing episode to another, but come, it is late and we both must dine at the Villa Kasbeck tonight with the Grand Duke Michael, the Prince of Wales will be there. Come another evening and I will tell you more.'

Life in the stately châteaux of France, the luxurious homes of the aristocracy in this period, was only to be compared with the palace of the sleeping beauty as depicted in Tschaikovsky's opera.

It was still entirely feudal, but it combined the beauty and elegance of the eighteenth century with what was thought to be the height of modern comfort; of course, the comforts of the nineties are considered to be decidedly primitive today.

One of the most magnificent of these residences was Dampierre, the residence of the Duchesse de Luynes, daughter of the Duc de Doudeauville, and his wife, *née* Mlle de Polignac.

Here the widowed Duchesse de Luynes maintained an almost regal state, receiving with pomp and ceremony the crowned heads of Europe.

When her husband was killed during the Franco-Prussian war, she set out, lantern in hand, to seek his body on the battlefield.

Her hunting and shooting parties were renowned, invitations to Dampierre were eagerly sought, but difficult to obtain.

Life there was gay and witty; only the most eminent men of letters were to be found amongst the guests.

Sometimes, having partaken of a sumptuous *déjeuner* on a table laden with treasures of silver, china, and glass, served by a veritable army of footmen, Yolande, Duchesse de Luynes, would step into her *équipage* accompanied by her guest of honour and lead a long cortège of carriages filled with pretty women in gossamer gowns with gay parasols, each with her *cavalier servant*.

They would drive along the grassy *allées* and shady rides, through the valleys of the Chevreuse which lay beyond the boundaries of the park with its ornamental lakes and canals, spanned by marble bridges.

Vallière, belonging to the Duc de Grammont, was another ducal residence whose owners held almost the status of reigning sovereigns.

I recall the Grand Duke Vladimir telling me of his impressions of this château, on his return from a visit to its owner, whilst he was still under the spell cast upon its guests, by the luxury and grandeur of life within its walls.

He told me that he was met at the station by carriages drawn by four grey post horses, perfectly matched, ridden by postillions, and escorted by outriders.

The château had some forty bedrooms, each with its own bathroom and w.c., an almost unheard of luxury at that time, the *salons* were filled with priceless *objets d'art*.

The shooting reminded him of Austria, the stables held horses for every guest. In the evenings dancing and music passed the hours away.

So it went on, the Doudeauvilles, Noailles and Rothschilds vying with each other to provide pleasure and entertainment for their guests.

My cousin, the Marquis de Villavieja and his brothers went one better, they rented the Château de Coubert.

Everything was superb, the shooting, the rooms, and the food. To outshine the rest, in their dining-room a footman in gorgeous livery stood behind each guest, his sole duty to wipe the rim of one's glass, every time it was used. This made me so self-conscious that I never touched my glass. The man behind my chair must have been bored to death, but as I was dying of thirst, I would rush upstairs as soon as we left the dining-room, fill my tooth glass with tap water and drink to my heart's content, sure that no eye watched me.

These châteaux, although very splendid and luxurious were not always very comfortable; there were some exceptions which did not provide every modern convenience.

I was told that Maeterlinck was invited to stay at one such house, his hostess telling him that a rest in really comfortable surroundings would do him good, and enable him to write his new masterpiece in peaceful surroundings. Overjoyed at the thought of weeks of relaxation, he set out for this haven of rest.

On his arrival, after a long tedious journey, he discovered that his hostess was out, so he asked the maid to show him to a certain necessary apartment.

'But certainly, Monsieur,' she replied, and she led him down a long stone corridor, stopping at length before what looked like a solid oak chair.

Smilingly, she unhooked a garment from the wall which proved to be a domino, then handing him a black velvet mask, she said:

'It is very practical, Monsieur, one slips on the domino, and wears the mask, then nobody knows who is sitting there.'

He was so aghast that he sent for the *fiacre* in which he had arrived, and left at once without seeing his hostess or wearing the domino.

This little incident reveals how entirely different is the French attitude to life as compared with that of the English.

The French are so absolutely natural over everything, but the English appear, in comparison, to be fenced in on every side by convention.

In the early nineties, the son of two of my English acquaintances arrived in Paris to study art. His family had pondered for months, as to whether he ought to go to live in such a hell of a city. They were strict and austere Victorians, and had brought him up shielded and secluded from the world, especially from women.

In due course, he descended upon Paris and was installed in a most respectable *pension* kept by an old English couple; the family thought that there he would be safe from danger.

The day came for his first visit to the atelier of the celebrated *maître* under whom he was to study. On entering the studio, his eyes fell upon the rather fleshy nude model, who was the subject posed for that morning's work.

As he had never seen a nude female before, it gave him rather a shock. Blushing violently, he sat down and tried to sketch the subject, feeling terribly embarrassed each time he glanced at the model, as though he were committing a mortal sin with every stroke of the pencil. Sitting next to him was a young girl, her hair hanging in ringlets, her features were most attractive. Quite naturally, she sketched, glancing at the model without a shade of dismay, even holding her pencil before her to measure the length of the limbs; presently she borrowed a stick of charcoal from him, next a tube of paint; then she criticized his sketch suggesting that his flesh tones were wrong, pointing to the model quite naturally, as though nakedness were the most ordinary thing in the world.

This led to questions as to where he came from, and of his family.

When everybody gathered their things together to leave for *déjeuner*, she said:

'Come with me, let us have lunch together.'

For a brief moment he hesitated, remembering all the advice he had received from his family on the subject of 'designing females', but again quite naturally she tucked her arm in his and led the way to a small café near by. The days passed very happily for these two, his knowledge of the French language improved, to his surprise he found that friendship with a French woman could be most delightful and intriguing, also that she had no desire to steal his money.

In a few days, again quite naturally, she invited him to her room.

She was gay and amusing but, oh, how different from his sisters and their friends!

That night, again quite naturally, they slept together. From that moment he was crazy in his love for her; they worked side by side, strolled side by side and slept in one another's arms. It was a perfect idyll.

The time for the holidays drew near, the thought of leaving her drove him to desperation. He wrote to his parents that he would not come home, he loved a charming French girl and they lived together.

This came as a thunderbolt to that prim Victorian household. His mother had hysterics; his sisters whispered to each other 'of the awful disgrace'; his father consulted the family doctor, the village parson and his solicitor, each of whom offered different advice.

Eventually, it was decided that Papa should leave for Paris at once to bring the 'erring boy' to his senses.

Meanwhile, quite oblivious of impending doom, Tom and Françoise laughed and sang the days away.

Papa arrived in Paris, complete with gladstone bag, a loud checked ulster in Scotch tweed, and a deer-stalker cap with earflaps. He looked around suspiciously as if expecting an *apache* to be lying in wait round every corner. He called a *fiacre* and showed the *cocher* his son's address written on an envelope. It was a long drive from the Gare du Nord to the Pantheon; when he saw the narrow street and still narrower house in which his son lived, he nearly collapsed; to him it seemed a veritable slum.

Just outside the door sat the *concierge* in his shirt sleeves, astride a broken chair. Again the envelope was shown, the *concierge* held up four fingers, indicating that it was on the fourth floor. So he climbed up the rickety stair till, at length, he came to a door on which were two cards, his son's and one with the name Françoise Leblanc hanging crookedly from a bent nail.

He knocked, there was no answer, so he opened the door. The room was small, just an attic. On the window-sill, a broken jug containing all the flowers of spring. There was one narrow bed with two crumpled pillows; a small table covered with a check cloth held a loaf of bread, some apples and a few radishes; the chairs were decidedly decrepit; there seemed no place to wash, but in the sunlight a caged bird sang merrily.

Gingerly he sat down and waited, fingering his collar nervously, perspiring at the very thought of what awaited him.

What would the village think? He thought of his home, the white-capped maid, his wife's relatives, all so correct in their behaviour. He thought of the Bank Manager, who had provided the money at a moment's notice with which to rescue his poor boy, from the clutches of a French harpy.

Just at that moment, he heard the sound of voices on the stairs and peals of laughter. The door was ajar, there on the landing he saw the culprits kissing each other passionately. His son looked up startled and dismayed, but the girl – and my word she was lovely – flew towards him and flung her arms round his neck. She gave him a resounding kiss on each cheek, crying:

'Tom! *C'est ton papa.*'

In a second, glasses were on the table, a bottle of *vin ordinaire* produced and poured out, and before he realized what was happening, he found himself kissing Tom. Why! he and Tom hadn't kissed for years, yet it had happened quite naturally. It was all so gay that he was swept off his feet: that night, all three dined in a small restaurant; later still, by now slightly tipsy, he was taken round the corner to a modest hotel.

Next day, he realized that it was all so natural, so beautiful: in youth love came and went, and really meant nothing. It was only when he thought of the explanations he would have to make to his wife that his heart sank; *au fond* what a lot he himself had missed in life. As Françoise had said: '*La Vie, c'est l'Amour.*'

In France, this phrase excuses everything. It expresses the fire and ardour of youth, it is the essence of poesy, it has the fragrance of spring flowers and is as spontaneous as a boy's first kiss.

In France, youth can have an *amie* and yet remain perfectly moral; in England it does happen sometimes, but the *joie de vivre* is lacking.

You find in France, a spirit of liberty which speaks louder than the mutterings of convention.

The pious old woman going to Mass is free, so is the naughty boy throwing stones, so are the amorous couple embracing in broad daylight under the very eyes of a *gendarme*.

Such is France, and one must accept her as she is.

'*L'amour nait dans un sourire, grandit dans un baiser, et meurt dans une larme.*'

Life seemed a long poem then, whether a Françoise Leblanc or a well-born lady, each in their own way would consciously or unconsciously live their life with only one desire, to love and be loved.

How *soignée* a French woman always was. She took care to look as beautiful asleep, as awake; no horrid greasy creams, no curlers, no hair net. A nightgown of finest lawn, almost entirely covered with real Valenciennes, fastened with wide satin ribbon bows; sheets and pillow-cases also of lawn, the former trimmed with flounces of wide lace which folded back on to the quilted cover, the pillows also edged with the same, but slightly narrower lace and similar bows of ribbon.

The occupant of this bed, would wear her hair in two plaits, framing her face and tied with the same satin bows.

The room would be a charming picture, for bedrooms were a veritable cult with the women of France. It was generally furnished with period pieces, pastel shaded Aubusson carpet, curtains and window hangings of the same delicate shade, muslin curtains criss-crossing the windows.

Above the bed, a round dome, from which fell the damask draperies which, encircling the couch, hung in fluted folds at the back, displaying an exquisitely carved crucifix. At one side lay a white sheepskin, on which rested two tiny fur-lined mules, matching the dressing-gown of *mousseline de soie* trimmed with cascades of lace – a perfect Watteau.

Of course, this is a picture of a woman of that era, who loved luxury, and took it all as a matter of course!

About eleven o'clock in the morning, her *femme de chambre* – shall we call her 'Julienne' – would gently wake her, draw back the curtains, tidy the room, then when her mistress had stretched and opened wide her lovely eyes, Julienne would place before her a silver tray on which stood a frothy cup of hot chocolate and a warm *croissant*.

Leisurely, she would open her *billets doux* and reflect.

Sometimes she would get into her bath, but in France in those days, people did not worry so much about that. However, she would take infinite pains to wash her small, well-cared-for feet in a footbath, if nothing more.

Julienne would then fasten her stays of pink *coutil*, and begin the preliminary lacing; it had to be done in relays.

Later, she would start doing the hair, building up a huge edifice, with pads made of horsehair, whilst her mistress would read a novel or study a poem.

At noon, she would be ready for *déjeuner* with Monsieur her husband. He and she would talk in a rather distrait manner as their real thoughts would be with their 'loves' of the moment.

Shortly after coffee, they would go their separate ways, he to his club, she to leave cards until about five o'clock, then each would go to their *rendez-vous*. They both knew all this, but as long as no scandals cropped up – all was well.

In the evening, Monsieur le Mari and Madame sa femme would be seen together, either at a big dinner or reception. What happened later was nobody's business.

It is, of course, the story of a certain type, and I may be excused from using it as an example.

Many young married couples lived quietly, and happily, but it was a devilish hard thing to do. Temptations seemed to lie in wait, as soon as one was resisted a greater one loomed ahead.

Men had no occupation. Work was a thing no gentleman ever dreamt of, so their only relaxation was gambling and chasing, not foxes, but *les femmes*.

Many of my readers will be shocked at the life I describe and some will say no wonder it had to come to an end: but has it?

In those days, the difference was that there existed no divorce in France. The lives of the children were not uprooted. They still had their father and mother living in the same atmosphere as themselves. It was an understood arrangement, that in the presence of their children no word of disagreement would ever be pronounced.

Now with divorce, so easily obtained, the children are thrown from one side to another – bewildered, they suffer.

Early in June each year, there took place an event to which every grade of society looked forward with excitement.

It was cheap, it was chic, so what more could one desire. This was the *Foire de Neuilly*. For days before it opened, carts, huge lorries filled with booths, wooden horses, organs and dismantled merry-go-rounds, could be seen coming from every quarter of Paris, up the Avenue de la Grande Armée to the Porte Maillot. These were followed by caravans filled to overflowing, with the owners of all these attractions.

People living over the shops in the vicinity, did not sleep for nights, on account of the noise and hammering, as the booths were erected.

When it was open, the din was beyond all endurance, as the *foire* went on both day and night, but the French will put up with anything as long as it spells money, and at the same time is amusing.

For Society, it was a kind of Ascot, parties were made up days ahead.

As it was generally warm and the air soft and caressing at this season, light *mousseline de soie* gowns or filmy dresses would be worn, large hats trimmed with ostrich feathers and ribbon, perhaps a gossamer wrap, barely covering the shoulders – really an excuse, so that if it was allowed to slip, her escort might gently and often tenderly return it to its place. After dinner, gay and elated with champagne, the party would set out for Neuilly.

As they drew near, borne on the still soft air came the blare of the merry-go-rounds, the shouting, laughter and the smell of the acetylene flares. Then one entered the streets of gaudy booths, passed the shooting range, heard the crack of the rifles, on to the lucky wheel to which one turned with excitement.

With wildly beating heart one followed the number, and hoped to win the crudely painted vase or jug depicting a woman dancing the *cancan*: at that moment it seemed positively of the utmost value.

Of course, no one ever seemed to win the *grand prix d'honneur* which, each year, stood in its accustomed place; usually it was a china basket with two kittens looking over its edge. How childish it all was; at any other time we should have thrown these ghastly objects on the rubbish heap, but in the atmosphere of the *foire*, they became art treasures.

Then climbing on to the wooden steeds of the merry-go-round, one would hold fast to the pole and whirl round, faster and faster, the men hoping to catch a glimpse of the women's ankles, and the women pretending to hold their skirts demurely in place, but carefully permitting a certain amount to be seen to entice the male companion. All around were the noisy crowds, the blare of the organs from the *petits chevaux de bois*, the men in spangled tights standing before each tent, shouting to attract customers.

All Paris came to Neuilly during the *foire*. The blaze of light! the noise! the music of the roundabouts, gave one a feeling of intoxication, under the spell of which one did the maddest things.

It was easy to become separated from the party with whom you had come. *Fiacres* were ever ready just outside and one could slip away for a while, returning with an air of innocence just in time to rejoin your friends.

It was all heavenly; the only drawback came when undressing that night and one had to catch the fleas one had picked up at the *foire*.

During these last ten years of the nineteenth century, France was torn asunder by *l'affaire Dreyfus*. It all began quite quietly in 1894 by the court martial of Capitaine Alfred Dreyfus, a Jew, who was convicted of passing secret military documents to a German agent. He was sent to the Devil's Isle for life and everyone thought that was the end of the matter, but it wasn't. Some time afterwards, a certain Colonel Picquart, an officer at the War Office, declared that he had discovered that the fatal document was not written by Dreyfus but by Major Esterhazy. He too was tried and acquitted, but Zola published an open letter to the President of the Republic entitled *J'accuse*.

At once bedlam was let loose. The public went mad. All sense of decency was forgotten, families were torn asunder, duels fought, anti-Semitic feeling flamed. Everyone took sides according to their personal convictions and it became positively dangerous to express one's thoughts aloud.

Dreyfus was brought back, retried, proved innocent, reinstated in the Army and later on even decorated with the *légion d'honneur*.

How typically French it all was. For a brief while, it was a cataclysm, then gradually the turmoil subsided and all was as though it had never happened.

18 MONSIEUR 'DE DION BOUTON'

In 1895, the relations between Britain and France for diverse reasons were not absolutely amorous.

Human nature so often craves for distraction, so why should anyone blame the Prince of Wales when he found it possible to slip away from Queen Victoria's jealous eye and cross the Channel, his thoughts quite naturally rested on Paris. But, of course, these visits had to be incognito.

Life, even in France, was gradually changing. Many of the great families had been obliged to close their châteaux, several of the friends of his youth were dead, but still the Prince enjoyed the life of that gay city.

The Marquis de Breteuil, the Rothschilds, the Marquis de Gallifet, the Prince de Sagan were ever whispering into his ear some new plan for amusement.

During these visits, the Prince had never ceased to take an interest in the inner working of French politics and the tempo of France.

Amongst all the distractions which were offered to him, he never missed visiting the Princesse Pauline de Metternich, who now lived much in Paris. There he would enjoy the wit and charm of that woman, no longer young, but who never failed to amuse him. He used to enjoy talking about his stay at their Schloss Konigswart, how wonderful the shoots, of the house party; alas so many had disappeared.

It was on one of his visits to Paris that he learnt it was the Princesse Pauline's birthday.

He ordered a huge basket of violets (the emblem of the Bonapartes) to be brought to her and on a card he wrote: '*En souvenir des temps des violettes.*'

That afternoon, he came to congratulate her. She was deeply touched, but exclaimed:

'So much fuss for an old woman of sixty, Monseigneur.'

'Surely that's no great age,' answered the Prince.

'Not for a cathedral but it is for a woman,' she replied.

To be at Auteuil on the *jour des dames* was heavenly. What toilettes! What excitement!

The ladies conscious of their beauty and importance would sit in their tribune or walk about on the lawns between the races, with only one object, to show off their gowns.

For most, the racing counted little; all that mattered was to see and be seen *par le monde*.

When we alighted from the four-in-hand in which, with a gay party, we had driven from Paris, the scene that lay before our eyes was like that of a select garden party.

Few *demi-mondaines* appeared at Auteuil, it was really a meeting for *les femmes du monde*.

The *tribune des dames* where sat the ladies belonging to the Jockey Club, looked like a gorgeous flower bed, so exotic were the colours of the frocks, so gay the fluttering fans. It was delightful to sit there and look down upon the grass, where men in black and shining top hats and frock coats escorted ladies arrayed in all the colours of the rainbow, with parasols and feather boas to match.

Doubtless the racing was superb, but what appealed to me was the colour and gaiety of the people.

Longchamps was a totally different thing. For weeks before the day of the Grand Prix, which is held in June, every dressmaker in Paris, from the *hauts couturiers* of the rue de la Paix, to the little seamstress plying her needle on the fifth floor of a back street – none had time to sleep.

Women of Society spent fantastic sums of money providing themselves with gowns, hats and parasols for the occasion.

Then they would drive to the course in open carriages, the better to be seen by thousands who waited to admire or laugh at the dresses going by, the *demi-monde* outvying in style and luxury *les vrai dames*.

The men would drive down in their phaetons with a smart 'tiger' up behind, or take the whip of an immaculate four-in-hand with perfectly matched horses, their coats like satin gleaming in the sun, the top of the coach occupied by a gay party. Occasionally, we drew aside to allow a horsebox to pass and wondered if, perchance, it contained the favourite.

Le jour des dames at Auteuil was *élégant* but the Grand Prix at

Longchamps was a dazzlingly brilliant occasion, not only this but for the men it meant business, as the Grand Prix had a world-wide fame and every language could be heard on the course.

For the ladies, once more, it spelt clothes; above all, to be able to glimpse the latest fashions.

Mannequins *lancés* by the great *couturiers* walked about displaying the most daring models, conscious of the admiration they created and the gaze of hundreds centred upon them. Men, racing cards in hand, binoculars slung from their shoulders, hurried down to place their bets, then back to exchange a few sentences with whoever interested them for the moment.

Cocottes took this opportunity to show off their new keeper.

As the hour of the famous race approached, everyone returned to their place on the tribunes, a tense feeling of expectancy fell upon the crowds.

For a brief space, nothing mattered but the horses – every eye was upon the course – fame, fashion, envy, distrust and greed all ceased to matter. 'They are off!' Then, scarcely a sound till, with a thunder of hoofs, the field drew near, then pandemonium till the winning post was passed.

Groans and sighs almost swamped the exclamations of triumph and it was a study to note the satisfaction or despair on the faces.

The French do not hide their feelings; they don't care who knows what they think, *au fond* – why not?

When one remembers the luxury, the inexhaustible sums of money gushing like a torrent from the rich quarters of Paris, it seems inconceivable that it lasted so long. Wealth did not seem to count in these days, millionaires enjoyed their wealth and those with small incomes or none at all, enjoyed the hospitality of the millionaires, so all was in order.

Amongst the wealthy men was Baron de Hoffman, who possessed one of the most sumptuous mansions in the rue Tilsit, and who, renowned for his charming hospitality, had one of the best chefs in Europe.

All in France, from the highest to the lowest, loved food, and almost everybody who was anybody, had a good cook, either male or female.

There were some chefs so notable that when their master gave a luncheon or dinner party, the mouths of the invited guests would literally water, in anticipation of the delicacies they would savour.

Baron de Hoffman, or 'Hoffy' as he was called, being exceedingly wealthy, had engaged a celebrated disciple of Lucullus. He paid him an enormous salary, and his fame grew daily, but the accounts rose even quicker and higher.

'Hoffy' realized that even his fortune could not withstand the strain of the steadily rising bills.

As the Baron did not want to lose his famous chef, he carefully considered what should be done. He knew he was being robbed, and that nothing which adorned his table justified these fabulous bills.

So he sent for the chef and said:

'Chef, your dishes are beyond praise, I am delighted with your work, but the expenses are prodigious.'

The chef replied:

'Monsieur le Baron is too wise not to appreciate that I add my percentage to the accounts. I must provide for my old age.'

'So must I,' said Hoffy, 'and I shall have nothing left at this rate. Let us make a pact. I will pay you £1,000 a year above your salary, on condition that you do not rob me of one penny in the future.'

The chef agreed, saying:

'I accept, on my mother's head I swear not to defraud you of a single sou.'

They were both satisfied, and shook hands on the bargain. The chef remained with 'Hoffy' for over twenty years.

Being so often in England, I frequently met the Prince of Wales. It amused me to compare him to a chameleon.

How tactful, how clever he was in changing his nature to fit different occasions.

He could be royal and condescending, making the whole assembly positively vibrate with ceremony.

At other times, when dining with intimate friends, he would be full of *bonhomie* enjoying his cigar, shaking with laughter at rather *risqué* tales, then when in Paris, becoming absolutely *Gaulois* in his conversation and behaviour.

Once in the Capital of the gayest country in the world, he would throw off all pretence and only live for the moment.

The Prince of Wales determined to enjoy his liberty ere he had to shoulder all the burden and responsibility of kingship. As often as possible, he would journey to France to visit Biarritz, Cannes and, above all, Paris.

He seemed to become a Frenchman as soon as his train entered the Gare du Nord.

The City too, seemed to take on new energy. 'The Prince of Wales has arrived' would echo from one part of that lovely city to another, and so it would lay itself out to captivate still more, if that were possible, its beloved guest.

At one of the smaller and less chic restaurants, a place where only gourmets who appreciated good food were the clientele, where there was no music to distract attention from the marvellous dishes, where the plain wooden benches stood on a floor strewn with saw-dust, here the Prince of Wales occasionally made his appearance with one or two of his intimate friends.

The *maître d'hôtel* said of him:

'The Prince is so thoughtful and makes himself quite one of us, yet one never forgets that he is heir to the throne of Great Britain.'

The *cochers de fiacres* knew him well, as often when walking with a friend, he would hail one and drive to some private *rendez-vous* hoping not to be recognized, but he always gave himself away by handing the *cocher* a *louis d'or*, whatever the distance.

In the later nineties, there was much poverty and distress in the poorer quarters of Paris. Epidemics broke out and the city authorities were almost overwhelmed. The 'Soeurs de Charité' worked day and night, priests made appeals from the pulpits and Society awoke to the needs of their fellow citizens. Funds were opened, money collected and fêtes organized to swell the funds.

On 4th May, 1897, a fancy fair called the *Bazaar de la Charité* was being held in rue Jean Goujon. A flimsy building had been erected and most of the Society ladies were taking part, selling at the stalls.

It was all exquisitely decorated but there was no thought of making any precaution against fire.

Suddenly, no one quite knew how it happened, but there was a burst of flame. There was a cry,' Fire! Fire!' then a panic; everyone rushed to the exits but, alas, they were too few.

The Duchesse d'Alençon, who was patroness, kept her head and cried:

'Save the young girls first!'

She was magnificent in her lack of fear but she gave her life in her efforts to save others.

Hundreds perished in the flames. It was one of the most fearful catastrophes that I can ever recall, almost every noble family in France mourned one of its members. Mr. Jimmy Durham has kindly allowed me to copy a letter he received from his cousin, the Marquise de Gallifet, the great friend of the Empress Eugénie.

31, Rue de Constantine.

MY DEAR MR. DURHAM,

How kind of you thinking of me. I don't know why the papers had named me as having disappeared, it is true a great many people had seen me at the bazaar which I had only left three minutes before the fire began. I crossed, when going in, a cousin of ours who was burnt, and I also met a friend going to fetch her daughter, they were both burnt, so I consider myself very lucky, having got off in time. One goes nearly mad here listening to the descriptions of those who were saved but who remained so long blocked up, in a very small space with no passage by which to escape, and the bazaar burning between them and the street. There are a great many very much burnt. I went the day before yesterday and today to three funerals each day and you see cortèges of three and four *cercueils* going one after the other in the streets, of the same family. Paris will be very sad after all this, as really nobody could think of amusement.

Good-bye my dear young friend,

Yours very sincerely,
GEORGINA DE GALLIFET.

One lovely June afternoon, towards the end of the century, I was driving with Sasha in an open carriage. We were going slowly down the Champs-Élysées, when I saw quite a crowd coming towards us. Men and boys were running in the road, shouting and gesticulating wildly. From the midst of the multitude came a strange spluttering and chugging sound.

I wondered what could be the matter. Our horses began to plunge and rear so wildly that the coachman, with some difficulty, brought them to a standstill and the footman jumped down to hold their heads.

Then I saw that some sort of vehicle was approaching. The people gathering round hid its shape, but I could perceive two men perched high up on a kind of bench with a tiller between them by which they were steering this queer contraption.

They were arrayed as though for a journey to the Arctic regions, leather coats with fur collars, leather caps with ear flaps strapped under their chins, with heavy fur-rimmed goggles to protect their eyes.

They sat there with a tense expression, gripping that steering tiller as though their very lives depended upon it.

'Sasha,' I cried, 'what is that contraption?'

'It is one of the new horseless carriages,' he replied, 'they are called automobiles.'

'Do they go faster than horses?'

'Yes! my dear, they tell me that they go at quite six or eight miles an hour.'

I was thrilled, this was indeed speed. By now, the *véhicule* was passing; it certainly shook and quivered and threw up a lot of dust, but then one could always wear a dust coat and thick veil. I turned to my husband:

'Sasha. I must have one of these automobiles, they will be very *chic*. Just think how delightful it will be to go about so quickly. Everyone who counts will use them.'

Then he said something which I shall always remember.

'You are delighted at the idea of travelling faster than horses can take you. As for me, I am sad; it is the end of an epoch. From henceforth, life will lack all sense of dignity and repose.

'Try to imagine a Royal procession without the pageantry bestowed by gaily caparisoned horses, prancing outriders and the glamour of a cavalry escort.

'With the coming of this machine, life will flow at a faster pace,

Society will rush feverishly from one fête to another wearing itself out in its search for relaxation.'

Frankly, at that time, I did not understand what he meant, but as I look back at those years, I realize how right he was. The petrol motor did indeed change our mode of life.

Very soon there were quite a number of private automobiles to be seen. The streets, always noisy, became almost too dangerous to cross, but as yet there were no aeroplanes in the sky; that was a horror still in the future.

. I shall never forget my first drive in a motor car. A friend had bought a 'De Dion Bouton' and wanted me to drive with him to St. Cloud. The whole family advised me not to go, saying that I should feel faint if I drove at such a wild pace, but as always Sasha encouraged me.

Then came the burning question, how to dress for the occasion.

Although it was a hot day, I was advised to wear a fur-lined coat, as driving so fast there would be quite a wind.

Then I wore one of those immense flat bérets which looked like exaggerated pancakes; it was fastened on with huge hatpins. Over this was flung yards of thick veiling which covered the whole hat and fastened tightly under my chin. I wondered what would happen if I wanted to blow my nose, but was told to 'forget my nose', so that was that.

Like a lamb to the sacrifice, I was led by two maids down the steps to where the car waited for me. The street seemed to be filled with an excited mob waiting to see us start, probably they expected the car to blow up or something like that.

I bade a tender farewell to the family and my friend started pulling knobs. There were two or three jerks, a snort, and we were off at a mad speed down the Avenue Hoch at five miles an hour. When we reached St. Cloud I remember that I sent a telegram to reassure my anxious family.

One evening, twelve months later, I was sitting with my mother-in-law in her *appartement* in rue de Logelback when Sasha came in and said:

'I have just been told that in a month autotaxis will be on the streets.'

185

I screamed with joy; motor cars were still rare, only a few of our friends possessed them, but even to think of hiring a taxi instead of a *fiacre* was exciting.

But my mother-in-law looked serious and said:

'My dear children, remember you are welcoming the end of true *élégance*, but it may bring good; it will certainly sound the death knell of the *cocotte*.'

We were so astonished that we burst out laughing; in a way she was right.

Elégance went on but in a different manner. It was less subtle, and not so exquisite and the *cocottes* slowly passed from the picture; the new equipage had destroyed their *raison d'être*.

During the summer of 1897, Trouville and Deauville were ablaze with flowers; the green lawns sloping gently towards the sea beaches were gay with the varied hues of the summer dresses, hats and parasols, these stood as rivals to the floral parterres.

In the *bains des dames*, fantastic bathing dresses were the vogue; in this world of women, to wear *le dernier cri* was essential; for the moment, men counted for little.

In the casino, enormous sums were wagered daily as the wheels spun.

While all this frenzy was at its height, a young girl lay dying, not amidst the fashionable folk in crowded Deauville, but in the small, almost unknown town of Lisieux.

There in the Carmelite Convent on the hill, Soeur Thérèse, a young nun with lovely delicate features was dying of consumption.

She had become a Carmelite at the early age of fifteen, much against the wish of the heads of the Order, as no child of that age had been permitted to take the veil.

So resolute was she in her determination, that she sought an audience of the Pope and laid her request before him.

She was so persistent that at last she was admitted into the severest order of the Church. A few brief years of serene service, then at the age of twenty-four, her life on earth ebbed peacefully and in great sanctity to its close.

On the 30th September, 1897, she passed from this world, and was buried in the Convent grounds as so many had been before her.

It was not long before rumours spread throughout France that strange things were happening at the tomb of a little unknown Sister in the Convent of Lisieux. The story passed the frontiers of the country and circled the globe, thus the little Carmelite, whose last words epitomized her life:

'I shall pass my heaven sending down graces like rose leaves upon the world,'

became famous.

People of every tongue and colour learnt to love her and seek her aid.

Now, a basilica crowns the countryside, and pilgrims from every country in the world come to venerate Sainte Thérèse de l'Enfant Jesus.

Trouville and Deauville are still crowded, the bathing costumes are now so brief as to be almost exiguous, gambling continues and has risen to fantastic proportions, beauty queens, film stars and profiteers flaunt their riches before the world.

All this ephemeral panorama passes like a fantastic dream but the veneration of the Little Flower increases daily as she scatters in ever greater abundance the rose leaves of her Graces upon the world.

About this time, the Prince de Z. arrived in Paris. He was young, extremely good looking, heir to a great name and one who knowing instinctively every secret trick to captivate women was an exceedingly dangerous man.

Women fell like ninepins before his smallest caprice and speedily he became *le lion de la saison*. All this adulation did not divert him from his real aim. He required a fortune to regild his coronet.

As usual, in France, mothers, aunts and grandmothers started laying traps to entice this future holder of *un grand nom* on behalf of their daughter, niece or grandchild, as the case might be.

Well-known women of Society were approached to act as 'go-between' between 'money' on the one side and 'rank' on the other.

The young man was duly approached but well knowing the trump card he held, he was difficult of access.

At last, a young orphan of about sixteen with abundant wealth was proposed, but the 'go-between' candidly admitted that 'she is not beautiful but her eyes are kind and she has good hair! also perhaps she may improve.'

The young man told me the rest of the story years later, when we were dining *à deux* in a *cabinet particuliere*.

'It was arranged that I should meet her at the house of her grandmother. I must say that until the very hour of the visit I never gave her a thought but then suddenly, whilst I was driving in a *fiacre* to the rue de Varennes, I realized that the money I had scraped together to come to Paris was fast coming to an end. Something must be done and at once – from inquiries I had made, no one else even approached the fortune this girl possessed and I had heard that she would also inherit the fortune of her grandmother. Supposing she was not good-looking – well, one could not have everything.

'Whilst I was thinking this, we arrived. I knew the house; it was one of those sumptuous mansions which lay between a courtyard and a garden. As I rang the bell, my heart gave a curious thump. Was I selling myself? If I didn't, I would be sold by my creditors.

'The old *concierge* in his green and gilt *galons* livery, emblazoned with a line of medals, opened the *porte cochère* and I drove into the courtyard. He rang the visitors' bell.

'My interview with the grandmother was candid, to say the least. She frankly admitted that she knew why I had come and said that before sending for Antoinette (I liked the name), she would tell me all about her. She was a good girl, very shy, not over brilliant but certainly not stupid.

'There was no doubt that she was ugly, but she had a good figure, was clean in herself, her teeth were not too bad, though her complexion was rather sallow, and she had no bosom to speak of; however they might yet develop, but *enfin* she has an enormous fortune. "*Alors*, now that I have warned you, I shall ring." A footman appeared.

' "Ask mademoiselle to come down!"'

'As for me, by now I was in such a turmoil, I literally had to hold on to my chair lest I turned and fled.

'Then a child, a very plain child, walked in.

' "Come, Antoinette, I want to present the Prince de Z. to you."

'She stood quite still, and I went towards her. She stretched out her hand but from shyness or what I do not know, I saw that her eyes were filled with tears.

'She certainly was all that she had been described, but I kissed her hand and we all sat down. She wore a kind of blue dress which made her distinctly yellow – she was tall, terribly thin, and certainly flat as a slate.

'I talked, the grandmother talked, and Antoinette listened.

'At last, I could stand no more. I begged to be excused, I spoke of an appointment which must be kept and I left.

'I was too angry for words. What did they take me for. I would prefer selling toothpicks in the Avenue des Acacias than ever seeing that golliwog again.

'You know the rest, dear friend.

'In two months' time, the "Madeleine" with all its "Suisses" and music from the "Concert Colonne" were going full tilt, and I was walking down the aisle with Antoinette's hand in mine, and the whole Society following us.

'Then the bitter struggle to try to live with someone whose presence and every movement makes you shudder; there is only one issue – shut the door and leave. My one decent act was that I never touched a sou of her fortune. I left France and did not return until I heard that she had remarried.'

'But she could not marry in a church,' I said.

'*Oui, ma chère ami*, that night her door was locked and on my dressing-table lay a note: "Believe me, monsieur, you are as repulsive to me, as I feel sure I am to you."

'We were quits.'

Mr. Jimmy Durham reminds me of the Ball of the Season of 1897. It was given by Monsieur and Madame Jules Porges in their beautiful house in the Avenue Montaigne. During the Cotillon, huge ostriches were wheeled into the ballroom, their feathers proved to be fans mounted in gold.

Mr. Durham, very young then, was quite dazzled by all this glamour and overwhelmed when trays of gold cigarette cases appeared as gifts for the men.

He tells me an amusing story.

He was really in Paris to study, so lived with a French family in the Boulevarde Malesherbes. The son was supposed to be his 'crammer'; he was seldom at home, much to Jimmy Durham's joy, as it gave him entire liberty. But one day he asked the daughter of the house, 'why her brother was never to be seen.'

'Oh! What will you! He is doing *la fête*.'

Only in France could this happen and the family consider it quite natural.

Another *rendez-vous* of fashion, was the *Nouveau Cirque* which supplanted the old Hippodrome with its roman chariots and fantastic display.

The *Cirque* was smaller and had open boxes where the ladies sat well to the fore with their male escorts in the background. In reality it was supposed to be a great treat for the children, but its *raison d'être* was for the ladies to be seen with their beaux.

The two principal clowns were Footit and Chocolât, the latter, of course, a Negro.

They kept their audience convulsed with laughter with their quips and sallies; towards the end of the programme, which was changed almost daily and contained only turns of the highest quality, the arena gradually sank and water flowed in, forming a miniature lake, on which little boats appeared manned by monkeys and other animals dressed as sailors; then a veritable regatta took place.

It was all rather childish, but when a thing was considered chic, Society would go like so many sheep, their one thought to be seen and their new clothes admired.

How vividly I recall the last Christmas of the nineteenth century.

When we entered the Church of St. Philip du Roule for midnight Mass, the building was already quite full. Our chairs were in the front row. The only lights came from the red sanctuary lamps. which glowed richly from the darkness and the few candles flickering before the scattered statues in the side aisles.

On the left of the high altar, drawn curtains shrouded the crib from our gaze.

I glanced at my watch, the time was just five minutes to twelve. In the deep shadows, I could discern altar boys standing at different points around the church holding long staves with lighted tapers.

The only sound which broke the silence was the creaking of the prie-dieus as people shifted their weight.

Then a clock at the end of the building struck the first stroke of the hour, streaks of fire ran in all directions and, in a moment, the whole edifice was a blaze of lighted candles and white flowers. On the left, the curtains parted, in the far distance we saw the holy figures adoring the new-born Christ.

The sacristy doors were flung open, altar boys with white-gloved hands, in surplices of finest lawn, edged with lace, worn over their red cassocks, paced slowly two by two, the thurifers swinging their censors; then in gold-embroidered vestments came the priests, the organ pealed and the voices broke forth into triumphant Alleluia! Alleluia! and we knew that 'l'Enfant Jesus' had been born.

Eight days later, I attended the afternoon service of intercession for the future and thanksgiving for the past, which was just over. Only a few people had been present, now they had all left, intent on the celebrations of New Year's Eve.

I looked around; I was quite alone. I thought of those still alive who had lived during the latter years of this dying era. Did they regret, or were they pleased that the century was passing?

I thought of the Empress and wondered what her feelings

191

would be, and of all those others who had basked in the glory of her Empire, and suffered with its agony. What would the new century bring to them?

The students of the Quartier Latin and Montmartre determined to celebrate *le fin du siècle* by a stupendous *bal masqué*; they are famed for the verve and imagination with which they carry out the theme of the year. This year they had cast their mind towards the future, and their costumes, or the lack of them, were to be typical of the year A.D. 2000.

All the students of the Beaux Arts School were present, having paraded the streets beforehand arrayed in the most fantastic get-up.

In all these student balls, the maximum effect was achieved with the minimum of clothing. When midnight struck, and the new century was proclaimed, even that minimum was reduced, until naked men and women were revelling wildly, champagne glass in hand, welcoming the New Era of Freedom and Licence.

It is an old tradition of the Quartier that revellers must bathe in the fontaine St. Michel or even those of the Place de la Concorde before going home.

When dawn came, La Place de la Concorde might well have been the Garden of Eden, so many Adams and Eves were to be seen.

It was against the law, but it was a unique occasion. Centuries are not born every day, so Justice was blind; by the time the shops opened the only signs of revelry were a few shreds of chiffon floating in the marble basins of the fountains.

That same night, Sasha and I were with a large party when the clocks struck the midnight hour.

The bells of all the churches in Paris rang out, champagne glasses were raised and, amid deafening cheers, the new century was proclaimed.

My husband and I stood together. Silently he made the Sign of the Cross above my head and said softly, so that only I could hear:

'Whatever lies before us in our lives, our love will shield us.'

When I awoke on the first morning of that new century, 1st January, 1900, Sasha's words of the previous evening came to my mind, they sounded almost like a prophecy of a forthcoming doom.

I asked myself why? 'This twentieth century seems full of promise.

'Europe is at peace; it is true that the British have a small Colonial war in South Africa and that the Boxer rebellion is giving trouble in China, but all that seems far away; meanwhile I am told that commerce has never been so prosperous. God is good and I am going to wear a heavenly new gown from Worth tonight, what can be better?

'It is true that relations between Great Britain, France, Germany and even Russia are occasionally embittered by diplomatic pin pricks, but the wounds are so superficial that they leave no visible scars.'

So life went on, and what is more it gained speed, as if, somewhere behind the scenes, a phantom figure urged us on – 'Time is short! Go on! Go on!'

Paris that spring was enchanting. Really, people seemed happy to be living in a new era; it was *le dernier cri* to describe oneself as belonging to the twentieth century and already everything appertaining to the past was *démodé*; all looked towards the glorious future which lay ahead, progress was the watchword, the past was forgotten, to be modern was *très chic*.

Society was preparing for a season of unsurpassed splendour.

From every quarter of the globe, foreigners arrived to visit the *Exposition*. Hotels were full – true there had been *Expositions* before, 1855, 1867 and 1889, but this would surpass them all. Monarchs and Princes had notified their intention of visiting the Capital and Americans were arriving by shiploads, and it was these latter who really counted, specially in the eyes of the famous restaurants and the shops of the rue de la Paix.

That spring, Polo under the patronage of the Marquis de Villaveija was the *rendez-vous* of all the fashionable world; one sat on the chairs under the trees of that delightful ground at Bagatelle, arrayed in trailing gowns and large hats, and watched the game.

One gossiped madly of the latest scandal, slandered one's dearest friend perhaps, but all the time one glanced out of the corner of one's eye at some approaching man in the hope that he would take the adjoining vacant chair.

Then tea was served at the little round tables under gaily coloured umbrellas; it was really only coloured hot water but in France it is ever so. What did it signify, the only thing that mattered was the man sitting beside you

On the left side of the entrance to the Avenue de l'Impératrice leading to the Bois de Boulogne, was a large space filled with rows of iron chairs, some straight and very hard, others with arms which made them slightly more comfortable.

Towards five o'clock in the afternoon, they gradually filled; smart club men predominated, they had come to watch the effect of the large fortune they were spending on the luxuriously dressed women whose carriages drove by.

It gratified them to see their property (or what they fondly hoped was *their* property – one could never trust these females) driving past, resplendent in lace and feathers, scintillating with jewels, their laced-edged parasols daintily poised to shade their faces.

These men, old and young, ugly and handsome, would sit smoking and criticizing each fair lady.

These lovely frail creatures were usually accompanied by an ugly old woman in black, known as a *repoussoire* who served as a foil to the beauty beside whom she sat.

Behind the *Beau Brummels* I have described, gathered the bourgeois families, who delighted to watch *le beau monde* as well as the *demi-monde*. They sat there with their wives and children gazing with interest at the passing show.

Meanwhile the endless panorama drove by; the ladies of Society, the *cocottes* and the *haute bourgeoisie* in all types of vehicles from the magnificent *vis à vis* and *chic* victorias with matchless horses, to the high phaeton with the tiny groom in tight livery and shining top hat sitting with arms folded on the dickey seat behind his master.

This grandstand of chairs became known as 'La place des "Décavés" '. 'Décavés' signifying an idler or one who has nothing better to do. Of course, in those days, it was deemed to be quite out of the question to have anything to do, except perhaps to adorn the Army, or Navy, but it was even *plus chic* to do nothing but eat, sleep and seek the unknown.

As I look back upon the year 1900, it seems to have been a kaleidoscope of colour, golden sunshine, blue seas, black seas, green trees and André de Fouquières, amidst a medley of people whirling madly round ballrooms and leading fantastic cotillons. We never had time to sit, except for long hours of eating. Did we sleep? It must have been very little, as I cannot remember doing so; anyhow, it was heavenly.

André de Fouquières in his charming reminiscences tells us that he led over 300 cotillons before 1914 and what cotillons! I cordially agree with him when he says:

'Young people now think of them as a kind of *mardi gras* affair, with streamers, coloured balloons and perhaps paper confetti.'

Poor deluded youth, how little you know of the days when beautiful things existed and life was a throbbing reality. Suggestions for a *rendez-vous* to partake of the forbidden fruit were accepted or rejected in the soft glow of brilliantly lighted chandeliers and not in the gloom and semi-darkness of underground night clubs.

Now, beauty is relegated to the galleries of museums or the dusty corners of antique shops; our reality is that of the cinema and it is sheer luxury to partake of stale potato chips or unimaginative chippolata at a cocktail party.

But why try to destroy the ideals of the present generation if they are satisfied. In any case, the past cannot return. *Tout passe, tout lasse, tout casse. Hélas.*

The artists who had dominated the horizon during the seventies and eighties had passed away. Flaubert, Maupassant, Baudelaire and many of whom we have written had followed one another to the grave.

Another generation was compelling the attention of the world, one wondered would they attain the heights of renown reached by their predecessors – only time would show.

Amongst the authors recognized as outstanding were Marcel Proust, timid, but ever striving until he reached fame; Georges Ohnet and Paul Bourget, both of whom were then thought to be daring and terribly romantic, but today they appear as tiresome and unrealistic.

The *Demi-Vierge* of Marcel Prévost caused a scandal. It was a true but brutal tale which even in this sex-conscious epoch one cannot read without deep emotion. Pierre Loti charmed us all with his sentimental melancholia of the Breton country, while the works of Anatole France exuded an atmosphere of scepticism, but displayed a deep knowledge of human suffering. Claude Farrere introduced us to the romance of the East.

The artists of Montmartre had given place to Boldini and Madraso, the former with his portraits of elongated women, the latter idealizing his subjects but retaining a perfect likeness.

The opera was electrified by Caruso, Plançon with his glorious bass voice, the unforgettable de Reszke brothers, and world-famed Chaliapine, each in their appointed rôle, whilst the irresistible Zambelli danced lightly into the hearts of men.

At the 'Théâtre Français', its famous *sociétaires* captivated audiences with the magic of their perfect idiom. Bartet, the famous tragedienne who startled London in 1908, the Coquelin brothers and later Jean, the son of Coquelin the elder; the latter became renowned in *Cyrano de Bergerac*.

In the world of music, I recall Debussy, and the incomparable Ravel, with his 'Bolero' and 'The Pavane for a dead Infanta'. Many of his contemporaries aped his style, but few, if any, attained his genius.

At the 'Théâtre des Variétés' in those days, there reigned one of the most renowned actresses of the epoch.

She was young, attractive and well known for her life of 'devil may care'.

I recall that she was slim and wore a fringe, her dark hair was cut straight round her lovely perfectly shaped features. She always played rôles of the most *risqué* kind.

Her lover *en titre* was Samuel, the owner of the 'theatre'. Men were crazy about her and she did whatever she liked.

Some years later, a rumour spread around: Eve La Vaillière has left the 'Variétés', and this at the height of her fame. For a while no more could be learnt, and to console her many admirers it was said: 'Oh, it is only for a time', but as time passed and she never returned, the truth leaked out.

Eve had taken a château in the country for the summer. She came under the influence of the old Curé of a neighbouring village who converted her.

She desired to become a Carmelite nun but knowing her past they feared a scandal, so she lived the life of a recluse in a tiny cottage keeping nothing for herself, but spending all in helping others and passing hours in penance and prayer.

Paris was deliriously gay; quite unconsciously we were drawn along a path strewn with perfumed rose leaves which intoxicated, and at the same time, drugged the senses. The thorns we resolutely thrust aside despite their efforts to warn us of their presence.

Balls, theatres, opera, polo at lovely Bagatelle, that bijou château built by the Comte D'Artois in three weeks for his sister-in-law Marie Antoinette, pigeon shooting at Puteau, and in the cool of the evening, Vicomte Leon de Janzé had just inaugurated dinner and dancing.

Then there were masked balls at the Opera, racing at Longchamps and Auteuil, teas at the Ritz, dress shows, flirtations, scandals; *au fond* life was so fast that the latter caused little stir or flutter.

It seemed impossible to add anything more to the whirl of life when suddenly the Russian ballet held its première on 17th May, 1909, then at once it became a fantastic success.

Polo, *tir aux pigeons*, balls, teas, everything was forgotten and the French people went mad. Nothing before ever approached that first night at the Chatelet.

It was the first time a French audience had ever sat through a whole evening of ballet.

Ballet as part of an opera, enlivened with singing – yes, but ballet *pur et simple* never before – many were sceptical, even Sasha and I shared the nervous tension of many of the Russians who like us were to assist at that first presentation of *le Ballet Russe*.

I remember that the programme consisted of *Le Pavillon d'Armide*, *Festin* and *Prince Igor*.

The old theatre, where as a child I had been taken to see my first play (it was *Michel Strogoff*), had been transformed into a renaissance picture.

The columns were covered with velvet, plants and flowers filled every corner. We were breathless with excitement and not a little anxious.

Then Tcheréprine appeared. There was little applause, to me the audience seemed cold. He lifted his baton, there was a tap, the orchestra commenced his own great work *Pavillon d'Armide* and the curtain slowly rose revealing the magnificent scene amidst which Nijinsky, Pavlova and Karsavina revealed their art: one could not call it dancing, it was as though they never touched the earth.

At the first *entr'acte*, the audience, who had been held spellbound by their supreme artistry, lost all control; as the curtain fell, the shouts, yells and screams were deafening. All around, people were sobbing with hysteria – I shall never forget the scene. Comte Robert de Montesquiou, standing immaculately dressed with his buttonhole, white gloves and gold-knobbed cane, leading the applause; even the critics lost their heads and I saw Serge Diaghileff, director of this talented cast, smiling and shaking hands with all around him. Another group of wildly gesticulating friends surrounded Bakst, the artist and creator of costumes and scenery.

After that, I can recall but little of the actual ballet. I was holding Sasha's hand and crying softly.

For the rest of the Russian Season, as it was now called, Russian operas were performed on alternate nights. *Boris Godounov*, *Ivan the Terrible*, and *Prince Igor* with Chaliapine, Smirnoff, Kastorsky and Lipkovska in the title rôles, supported by a strong cast and a superb chorus.

Paris seemed transformed during those weeks, the very weather seemed to smile on those unforgettable artists. They were invited to many parties but few invitations were ever accepted.

Diaghileff saw to it that they should never relax whilst they were working. The life of ballet dancers is one long devotion to their art.

That year, everything Russian became the rage, all was *à la russe*.

In the two years which had elapsed since his accession to the throne, King Edward VII had done much to modernize his Court, but the tiresome thought that followed him constantly, was the strained relations with France.

In Paris the feeling towards Britain was definitely hostile and sometimes disagreeable episodes occurred.

One day, my brother and I were entering a restaurant. I had become very careful and always spoke in French; he, not thinking, asked me in English where I would like to sit.

Two women at a table close by hissed:

'Down with the English, they come to annoy us!' whilst someone else shouted '*perfide Albion*'. My brother, very tall and brave, took not the slightest notice but my legs nearly gave way.

It was about this time that King Edward decided to come to France.

I remember the Government; Loubet was Président and Delcassé the foreign minister. They realized that all the feeling against Britain on account of the Fashoda incident and the Boer War was obsolete, and that France would benefit greatly from an alliance with Great Britain.

All this was tactfully conveyed to the King and he decided to see what he could do, much against the advice of his ministers who feared that his reception might be hostile.

On 1st May, 1903, the King arrived. He wore a scarlet uniform, which seemed to act like a red rag to a bull, on the French mob. He entered an open carriage to drive to the British Embassy, it was his first State visit to France as King-Emperor.

We stood at a window to see the procession. Several members of the Embassy had told us of their anxiety, so I prayed as I stood at that window.

Then he passed smiling, gracious and truly regal, but there was a slight disturbed look in his eyes. We could hear cries and shouts from the crowd, '*à bas les anglais*', '*vive les boers*', '*vive le Colonel Marchand*', but His Majesty continued smiling and saluting. It was only when he reached his destination, that the strain he had gone through was obvious to those around.

Somehow through it all, one realized that there was never a

word of personal insult – it was Britain the crowd wanted to abuse, and they had to do it through him.

The King seemed to convey that he understood their point of view, and gradually that feeling permeated the heart of France.

They could not really forget the fifty years of constant admiration and *camaraderie* of *le Prince de Galles*. It was his charm that during those critical four days of his visit regained the hearts of a fickle nation.

He attended, like any other august visitor, the Gala at the Opera and was received at the Hôtel de Ville. It was his speech there that conquered the nation.

When we again went to that window, I forgot to pray.

As he passed through the streets, the same mob who had hurled insults now yelled themselves hoarse, '*Vive Edouard Sept*'. '*Vive notre ami et roi*'. The King was waving his hand quite informally, and we sensed that the love and charm of Paris was warming his heart anew, as it had done ever since that unforgettable evening in 1855, when he had stood with the Emperor on the terrace of the Tuileries, and his youthful heart was intoxicated by the spell of that city which never allowed him to stray far from her alluring graces.

We have talked of social life and of politics, now let us turn to the religious life of the country.

In all the splendour of the Empire and the hustle for power that followed with the Republic, it was hardly realized, even amongst those living in France, that the germ of an anti-religious trend was developing within the Government. To discover the first traces of this evil malady it is necessary to go back to the year 1850.

There was a small village, Mazières en Gatine, in the Canton des Deux-Sèvres; it was almost unknown to the outside world.

Its population, of about a thousand, was scattered through the district.

Its roads were no more than tracks crossing the fields, its houses built on the rough ground contained only the one room.

The farming implements crudely made by the peasants were of little use; yet, life was happy.

Each morning before starting work, the husband and wife, surrounded by their children would kneel to pray, each evening after supper, they would once more kneel to give thanks for the blessings of God. On Sundays, they went to Mass to listen to the old Curé.

Their only meat was salt pork.

In summer on feast days, there was dancing on the village green; in winter, during the long evenings neighbours gathered round the tallow candle, the women to weave, the men to plait straw.

It is true that there was a school, but the peasants, themselves ignorant, unable to read or write, did not trouble to send their children. The schoolmaster, indolent by nature, was only too pleased not to be bothered, so everybody was happy.

This isolated community had very little communication with the outside world, even when Napoleon III made his *coup d'état*, nobody at Mazières en Gatine took any notice.

Then a school for farmers was created, and little by little the silence was pierced.

New roads were built, the railway came to the end of the valley bringing produce to and fro.

The inhabitants began to spend more upon clothes, to eat off earthenware, to drink wine and to partake of meat on feast days.

A wine shop was opened, a doctor appeared, then a veterinary, presently a lawyer and last of all a magistrate was appointed.

After 1872, the young men did their military service and thus were initiated into a life which dazzled them at first; the stories they told on their return home, amazed their friends and relations.

Slowly the danger grew, morning prayers were forgotten, evening prayers still muttered but not on their knees, mostly gabbled as they flopped on to the feather beds.

The good Curé still exhorted, persuaded and preached, still his flock were baptized and made their First Communion, or received Extreme Unction but the anti-clericals were gaining ground.

In 1881, Jules Ferry was determined to eliminate the religious influence from France. When asked by Jaurès: 'What is your aim?' Ferry hesitated for a moment, and then made the famous answer:

'My aim is to organize humanity without God or King.'

He was bent on 'de-christianizing' France during his four years of office.

He realized that the enormous power of the Clerical party emanated from their control of primary education.

All religious teaching was forbidden, and most of the religious orders were dissolved and exiled from France.

A few were unmolested, but in 1886 even those were given a few days in which to submit to civil control or to go.

Nuns who had devoted their lives to service in the hospitals were replaced at a moment's notice by anyone who chose to accept the job.

Chapels were closed and property which had belonged to the Church for centuries was ruthlessly seized by the State.

I can recall the most poignant scenes which took place in the schools, the children fighting like young tigers, kicking and biting the men who came to take down the crucifixes, holy pictures and images.

In Normandy, Brittany and many rural *départements* there were pitched battles, the inhabitants using force and even shooting anyone from the Government who came to apply the new laws.

The most pathetic scenes were witnessed when the convents were closed and the nuns, some very aged who had not left the cloister for years, were driven forth; the enclosed orders too of women who had given their life to prayer. All these with only a few days' warning, were thrown into the street, without visible means of existence.

They were brutally informed that they must abandon their 'habits' and wear civilian clothes; this was impossible as they had none, but charitable people came to their assistance and supplied their necessities.

Their hair was short and they feared victimization if they were seen, so some wore caps or peasants' handkerchiefs tied under their chins, or even old-fashioned bonnets.

A few returned to their families, but they were made to feel that they were unwanted; another mouth to feed.

They tried to go into service, but no one would engage them, a few succeeded in becoming governesses, but in spite of their tribulations, they all tried to keep to the rule of their order.

The Government knew only too well that as long as these holy souls remained to manifest to the world by their lives and teaching that God existed, the State would never be quite supreme.

Troops were forbidden to enter churches, public prayers were suppressed, Army chaplains abolished, the obligation to keep Sunday as a day of rest was swept away, not to be restored until twenty-five years later.

I remember, about this time, going to visit a poor woman in hospital; there was little I could do, she was so desperately ill. When on the point of leaving, I asked her if there was anything she needed, she begged me to give her some 'two sou' pieces.

I was astounded and wondered what she could need them for, for, as I remembered that when the hospital was administered by the nuns, nothing was lacking.

The poor soul lifted her pillow, and there lay a little pile of coins, she assured me that nothing could be obtained without giving the *soi-disant* nurses something.

A glass of water, or the most elementary service, it was all the same, one had to give a *pourboire*.

These women had never been near a sick person before and resented helping those who were suffering, until they were ordered to do so, and no one was washed, the linen never changed. It seemed quite incredible, but I verified that all she said was only too true: most of these women were street-walkers too old to do their trade.

The Authorities worked hard in the villages to destroy the Faith, but at times they were foiled.

In one village I knew, the chief landowner was a wealthy Polish nobleman, Monsieur Yourievitch.

Hearing that the anti-clericals were coming to secularize the district, and to intimidate the people from performing their religious duties, he made it known that the parents of each child baptized in church by the Curé would be given 1,000 francs.

It was not long before the anti-clericals realized that he had defeated them and they discreetly withdrew.

The end of the long battle with the Church came in 1906 when Briand, Minister of public worship in Clemenceau's Cabinet, separated Church and State.

It is curious that despite this separation and the attacks upon the Christian religion, the Faith of the people is still strong.

Today in France, religious orders flourish. Convent schools are open to all and nuns nurse the sick.

During the months of May and June, the children who had made their First Communion appeared on the streets and avenues of Paris.

The Champs-Élysées seemed filled with diminutive brides, little girls in muslin dresses almost long enough to hide their white kid shoes, their fine lawn veils floating in the breeze, the heads crowned with a circlet of white flowers. They walked so demurely, ivory covered prayer book in their white-gloved hands, a glass and gold rosary entwined around their small wrists.

The little boys were dressed in black trousers and short jacket with snowy-white waistcoat, and Eton collar.

On one arm, they proudly bore a white armlet tied in a large bow, with silver fringe. They also wore white gloves and carried prayer book and rosary.

All Paris seemed filled with the flutter of angels' wings, as these small children walked about; there were so many of them, surely their guardian angels could not have been far away.

Always it seemed to me that they were followed round by hosts of admiring relatives, proud parents, aunts and uncles, all up from the country for the great day.

Most of them were in deep mourning with heavy crêpe veils, even the men had crêpe armbands and hat scarves. To be in mourning seemed a great part of their lives; even for the most distant cousin, women enveloped themselves from head to foot in veils of heaviest crêpe.

After Mass, they all gathered in a restaurant for a breakfast, sometimes they would have to wait for Monsieur l'Abbé or the Curé.

Speeches were made and everybody wept copiously into black-edged handkerchiefs, even the little First Communicant sobbed, overcome with the emotion of the occasion.

Doubtless he or she understood but little of the beautiful speech pronounced by *l'oncle Jacques*.

Then all would walk or drive to the Bois de Boulogne or the Champs-Élysées to promenade in state.

About half past three in the afternoon, the whole party would return to the church, where amidst a scene of flowers, incense and music, the baptismal vows would be renewed and the benediction given.

It was all very touching and beautiful; there was still belief and sceptics were rare.

Although much gaiety mingled with the holiness of this sacred occasion, the holiness lingered in the child's heart and even if later it was disturbed for a while, it was never entirely lost.

In these days, I cannot say it is lost, but certainly it is overlaid by the synthetic worldliness engendered by Hollywood films.

Sometimes as I think of those golden days in Paris I remember how, when returning early in the morning after a ball, we would go to early Mass on our way home, so that we should be free to sleep on until luncheon.

I wonder how an English congregation at early service would react if a car stopped at the porch and out of it stepped women, wearing tiaras and full evening gowns with pearls and diamonds, accompanied by men in evening dress with the flower still in their buttonholes and opera hats under their arms: to walk up the aisle, kneel quite naturally and take part in the service.

The parson and congregation would be horrified and consider it an outrageous act of blasphemy.

In Paris this was a thing we often did. We knelt amongst the usual mixed congregation of women on their way to market, workmen hearing Mass before going to their job, nuns escorting school children, often women of the streets, returning from their night's work. Some, alas, quite young, others old and haggard.

No one even glanced up as we entered; all were intent on their own private devotions, not caring one jot about those around them.

I remember taking a small French girl to a service at the English church in the rue d'Aguesseau. Coming out, she turned to me and asked rather naïvely; 'Was it a concert?'

'No,' I replied, rather astonished at her question.

'Then why do they sing all the time?'

I tried to explain the ritual but somehow she didn't seem to understand and then she said:

'Don't they ever speak to God privately?'

This seems to me to explain the whole attitude of the French people to their religion.

The Church is the home of God and they go to see HIM: pay Him visits and kneeling down in their working clothes and with their shopping bags beside them, speak to Him quite naturally of their family affairs.

The old Curé de Campagne was entirely a feature of France; nothing quite the same exists in any other country.

If you happen to have read *l'Abbé Constantin* you will understand what I mean.

He was the father of his flock, so entirely one of the family that no reunion was complete without his presence. One met the good priest walking down the village street, his *soutane rapé* buttoned down the front, a wide silk sash across his well-filled stomach, for he loved good food washed down with a glass of red wine.

He wore thick-soled shoes with a silver buckle, and carried a stout stick which he did not spare on the backs of naughty boys.

He walked endlessly, visiting his parishioners in the distant farms, admonishing, advising and comforting. Knowing the most intimate details of their lives, he would scold the husband, rebuke the wife and yell at the children, but all would love and obey his every word. Nothing took place without Monsieur le Curé being present.

He usually had an old cook to look after him, who scolded him furiously if he gave away too much of his scanty means or came in late for his frugal supper.

It was all very simple and truly rather beautiful; his people were peasants, he also was a peasant, so they understood one another.

A première at any of the principal theatres of Paris was a great event. There was so much more leisure, and people had time to appreciate the true value of art and literature. Audiences were criticial – the success or failure of a play turned upon the use of an appropriate gesture or phrase.

Often the author would be asked by a well-known hostess, to read his work to a select audience, before it was produced. She would arrange her drawing-room so that her intellectual guests could form a favourable opinion in comfort.

The author usually arrived when all were seated. After the never-failing ritual of kissing the ladies' hands and enthusiastically shaking those of the men, he would sit down amidst a deathly silence, take from a portfolio innumerable sheets of manuscript, clear his throat, take a sip of water from a glass placed beside him, and start. Sometimes it would take hours. I disliked these performances as I hate being read to, and not being able to leave the room, or even cough, made me nervous. Towards the end, my mind wandered, and I could no longer concentrate.

I feel sure most of the listeners felt the same, but at the end of the 'seance', when the author had gone through joy, sorrow, agony, and, at last, achieved peace – as nearly always books and plays have to end well – everybody would rise, shriek, wave and nearly injure their hands with clapping, bravo! bravo!

It seemed like a resurrection, as many had slept soundly the whole time.

When the play was produced, it was fantastic; every box and every seat had been booked for weeks beforehand.

All the *élite* of Paris would attend, everyone at fever heat, the knowledge that all who counted would fill the theatre was another attraction; each *entr'acte* would augment the excitement.

The tempo of the public that night, decided whether the play was a success or failure. All this counted for so much then, the authors of plays or books, actors and singers were the theme of conversation.

Society had to talk, politics changed so rapidly that people had barely time to form an opinion before the Government had fallen, so few took an interest in the country.

When autumn came, men prepared for the wonderful 'shoots' which many of the famous châteaux offered them.

On the whole, France is not a country devoted wholeheartedly to sport, apart from a select few who spend the whole season shooting in different countries.

As for the women, most of them neither knew nor cared anything about it, unless they had been to Scotland and seen 'a grouse', then they would return to their native land determined to go in madly *pour le sport*.

They would array themselves in fearsome tartan tweeds, tyrolese hats with a pheasant feather and high-laced but very ornate boots and would follow *ces messieurs* at a respectful distance.

How different from an Englishwoman 'out with the guns' in her well-worn suit, with a cap pulled half-way down her head and thick-soled shoes.

It is amusing as well as interesting to pause and consider the evolution of subjects which has gradually developed, beginning with the First World War, and continuing to our own time.

In those days, everyone knew their place, from the highest to the lowest. In large establishments, it was a complete hierarchy – the head servants were like kings and queens, the lowest scarcely dared lift their eyes towards them, but they knew that in time when they had gone step by step up the social scale, from washing the back steps and then being gradually raised to stone the front steps of the mansion, their career had started. And so it had. They realized that the head steward and the omnipotent housekeeper, in her black satin and gold brooch (the latter had been presented to her on completion of the first twenty-five years of her service by the Duke, or Marquis, she had served) she, too, had once knelt in the street on a rough square of carpet, just large enough for one knee, to wash the area steps – just as Anne, the seventh housemaid, was doing now.

The valets and lady's maid travelled with their employers for week-ends. Each Saturday, of course, there was much packing and unpacking but as all had been ironed and prepared before leaving,

Sunday was really a day of leisure, except for attending the lady during numerous changes of clothes. But what style was maintained in the housekeeper's room! What etiquette! How genteel it all was and how grand!

In the servants' hall, it was equally nice, as directly the nobs had retired to that most sacred *appartement*, the housekeeper's room, they could talk and let themselves go. The ladies' maids would wear slightly *décolleté* dresses, the valets all wore dress suits.

The lower maids would have fun amongst themselves, intriguing flirtations with the numerous footmen. Naturally, none would wear colours, all dresses were in black, even to go out, except the housemaids, in the morning when working, they would wear coloured prints. In the afternoons, they looked very neat in their black gowns with little lace collars. Somehow, all worked willingly, knowing they were working to get on.

Now, all are trying to get on without work. There is such a restless feeling, the one maid one has, is an agony, everlastingly she knocks at the door to ask if she can go out, or goes without asking; then her one idea is to copy a film star from *Vogue*, so all her spare time, which seems to augment each day, is spent in sewing cheap but fantastic coloured stuff into equally fantastic-looking clothes.

Nobody is satisfied, the mistress looks aghast when the maid comes in with tea, fearing that her guest should think she was harbouring a *quart de mondaine* – and the *quart de mondaine* is disappointed no one admires the multi-coloured dress. *Au fond* all is dissatisfaction and false values.

Paris, London, St. Petersbourg, the Triple Entente! vied with each other in gaiety, but Paris stood above all. Every nationality seemed to be congregated here.

The leaders of English Society, the beautiful Marchioness of Ripon, the Duchess of Leinster, the Countess of Warwick, and Millicent Duchess of Sutherland.

From Russia came Princesse Olga Orloff, Princesse Susie Belosellsky, Comtesse Koutosoff, Comtesse Betsy Shouvaloff, each in their own way more beautiful than the women of France, yet these latter carried the day. They were vivacious, witty, supreme in the art of conversation and far more subtle in the wiles of attraction.

These different types from the countries of Europe made the French capital a galaxy of interest.

One day, I was lunching at 'Henri's' in the Place Gallion, which was then considered perfect for a connoisseur of food. We were a small party. At a table near by sat three women, Lady de Grey later Marchioness of Ripon, Comtesse Betsy Shouvaloff and the Comtesse Laure de Chevigné.

Amongst our own group was a young Spaniard, an artist.

He was so impressed by the picture these ladies presented as symbolic of their respective countries, that he could scarcely swallow a morsel.

Lady de Grey stood for the perfect type of English *grande dame* – tall, with regular features and dignified bearing, sure of her lineage and unquestioned superiority, gracious and condescending, a true emblem of her native land.

Comtesse Betsy Shouvaloff, handsome with slightly high cheekbones, the typical aristocratic Russian *boyarinia*, knowing her unchallenged position in Russian Society defied all competition.

Then the French Comtesse, one of the acknowledged chic women of French Society, versatile, quick, slightly *mordante*, knowing that with a nod of recognition she could lift an unknown person to the height of notoriety, ignore them and they would feel that they had lost all hope.

I noticed my Spanish friend drawing on the back of his 'menu' – presently he passed the sketch to me, underneath he had written:

'The Three Graces – but no apple would be golden enough for their acceptance.'

At that time, no smart woman dare to be seen in a tram or omnibus. I can still recall the pangs of agony I suffered on one occasion, when I transgressed this convention.

We were living in our *apppartement* in the Avenue Henri Martin at the time, and Zoia's governess persuaded me to go with them in the tram down to the 'Trocadéro'.

I was simply terrified lest someone should see me. Suddenly

the tram stopped and Comte Jacques de Pourtalès got in; it was quite all right for men to be seen in a public *véhicule*. The tram was almost empty and he sat down right in front of us. At first he was busy searching his pocket for a few sous with which to pay his fare, so he did not perceive me.

I had seen him at once; indeed it was impossible not to do so but I completely lost my head, and began talking wildly first to Zoia, then to Mademoiselle, turning my head to the right and left, looking most earnestly at each in turn, anything rather than look in front of me.

As the Comte knew me intimately, he must have been completely baffled, and wondered exactly what was happening, or what he had done.

By this time, I was rapidly becoming hysterical. I looked wildly at the window behind his head, till at last I could stand it no longer, I flew to the door, rang the bell and jumped off the tram, followed by Zoia and Mademoiselle.

A few nights later, I met him at a dinner. He said:

'For Heaven's sake. What happened the other day? I sat in front of you, and you simply refused to look at me!'

Of course I swore that I had not seen him, but he, a witty and subtle Parisian, looked at me archly and murmured:

'I fear a little British snobbery, *hein*?'

Even during the so-called 'Naughty Nineties' it would have been quite impossible for a woman to smoke in public in Paris.

Men did not smoke in a carriage or in the street, or when they were accompanying a member of the fair sex. Ladies smoked very little in those days even in the secrecy of their boudoir, everything about a woman had to be so refined and the very idea that even a suspicion of cigarette smoke might linger on her breath, was unthinkable.

Now, women simply do not care, they smell as do the men, of rank tobacco and even of spirits. They don't smell each other. In the old days, when love meant all the enticement of attraction, nothing was allowed to mar it.

People did not take so many baths, it is true, but the care a woman would bestow upon her body, replaced these daily submersions, when people jump in and out again, and when they are content to wear their gowns with nothing else between the material and their skin.

In those days, there were stays, then the *cache corset* and for the afternoon, a small *baptiste fichu*, so that the material of the dress should not touch the body.

Now, nothing like that exists, and girls are delighted to inform you that they wear nothing under their frocks; those same frocks in which they have danced and felt far from cool.

All this may bring down the wrath of the young and even of some of the older women on my head, but it is the truth.

Let us now return to the eventide of the Empress. The Marquise de Gallifet's idea had proved a success. Eugénie passed many winters in the Villa Cyrnos at Cap Martin, where Queen Victoria had often visited her, but as soon as the spring came the Empress would travel back to England, always breaking her journey in Paris.

Over the years, her relations with Princesse Mathilde had softened, the Princesse had become old and feeble, and Eugénie would visit her at her Château de St. Gratien.

During her visit in September 1903, she realized that the Princesse had not long to live. She sat by her bedside, and they talked and recalled things that only they had known.

The Princesse when saying good-bye seemed sad. At that moment, the sun broke through the mists and flooded the room with its light. The Princesse Mathilde seemed to revive and exclaimed:

'It is the sun of Austerlitz.'

As Eugénie left St. Gratien, she uttered a phrase which might well have been the epitaph of the Princesse.

'A generous soul is passing from this world.'

Princesse Mathilde retained her strong personality to the end. She died on 4th January, 1904.

Eugénie loved to surround herself with youth. Was it to remind herself of what might have been if her son had lived?

She had lost so much; she had now no child, no grandchild, so her friends' grandchildren seemed to fill the great void in a way.

That is why Lord Carisbrooke so often stayed at Farnborough with his mother, Princess Beatrice. How many times during those long evenings after dinner, Eugénie must have thought when looking at this young man: 'If only he could have been the son of Louis'?

There is little doubt that the Prince Imperial hoped that on his return from the Zulu War when he had gained fame, Queen Victoria might consider him worthy of her charming daughter, but death touched him and all ended. Lord Carisbrooke told me that he once asked his mother, Princess Beatrice, who had married Prince Henry of Battenburg, if she had ever been in love with Louis Napoleon?

She hesitated and without committing herself, replied: 'I had not then met your Father.'

A delightful answer!

He told me that once when staying with the Empress, she took him down to the coachhouse which she was arranging as a Napoleonic Museum. As they stood looking at the carriage in which she and the Emperor were driving on the night of the Orsini outrage, impulsively she stepped into it, and made him sit beside her.

She showed him where two loaded pistols were always kept, but strangely enough when she sought for them on that fateful night, they were missing.

'Surely,' said Lord Carisbrooke, 'you would not have used them?'

The Empress looked at him with surprise: 'Certainly I should have fired,' she replied.

At Farnborough, which had been bought after the death of the Prince Imperial, the Empress would sit during the long evenings, dressed in deepest black and play 'patience' whilst the Duke of Alba, her great nephew, and Monsieur Pietri talked quietly. The form of patience of which she never seemed to weary was that with which the Great Napoleon whiled away his melancholy days in exile on St. Helena.

She would never allow anyone to read to her after dinner, but enjoyed discussing politics, and often baffled her visitors by the depth of her knowledge.

The Duke of Alba in his address to the Institut Français de Madrid, described these evenings, and spoke of his aunt's curious custom of wearing five wedding rings – her own, that of the Emperor, her father's, her mother's and, last of all, her sister Paca's.

She enjoyed amusing anecdotes and frequently entertained her guests with reminiscences from her past. Sometimes, the conversation flagged, but the Duke knew a sure method of starting it again.

He had only to state: 'Garibaldi was not as powerful as generally supposed.' This phrase was enough to cause the Empress to lose her temper, and words flowed like a torrent from her lips.

Thus time passed until the clock chimed eleven, when the Empress would rise and bid them all 'good night'.

Eugénie was profoundly religious without being a bigot: she was superstitious and dreaded Sundays as a day full of omen in her life; her father died on a Sunday, on such a day the Empire fell; her son died and, strangely enough, she herself died on a Sunday morning.

Slowly but surely, the years passed; often she travelled abroad on her yacht. As she grew older, her restlessness increased and she seemed almost afraid of remembering too deeply

Eugénie loved the sunshine and flowers of Cap Martin, perhaps the light was too fierce for those lovely eyes which had wept so much and thus gradually, the sun seemed less brilliant, the flowers less gaudy and the shadows increased until almost darkness reigned.

Farnborough Hill, with the tombs of her dead almost at her very door, seemed at times overpowering to the Empress. She was a wealthy woman, and could afford to indulge her whims, so she purchased a yacht, which she named *Thistle*. It was small, and although her advisers had besought her to buy a larger vessel with facilities for greater comfort, as usual, she insisted on having her own way.

The Empress was a wonderful sailor, but alas, the members of her suite were not so fortunate. The very mention of a sea voyage made them positively sea-sick, as they recalled how the *Thistle* would pitch and roll if there was the slightest ripple. Such was Court life.

Eugénie often said:

'I never feel so well on earth as when on the top of a wave.'

Some of the guests on these voyages told me that the Empress would begin to glow with health, as soon as she reached 'that awful skiff'. The more it rolled, the straighter she seemed to walk and yet she was drawing near to her ninetieth year.

During one of her last visits to Paris, on her way to 'Cyrnos' she insisted on visiting Compiègne.

It required courage, but as old Duperré told me: *'Elle était toujours une indomptée.'*

So, accompanied by the Princesse de la Moskowa, she passed from room to room 'incognito' and only when reaching a certain bedroom, did she falter. There it seemed as though a small boy stood before her, laughing and stretching out his arms. It was but a fleeting vision in her son's room.

The Empress Eugénie became more restless as time went on. She told Mélanie de Pourtalès once, she felt sure this unaccountable urge for change of scene came from her mother, who ever craved for the moon.

During her travels, the Empress visited Italy, but when there she refused to meet the King, Victor Emmanuel, as she never forgot that he had not even the decency to remove from her view a huge photograph of the German Emperor in all his paraphernalia, which was standing on a table in the drawing-room in which he had received her soon after 1870.

She really loved the sea and on a beautiful sunny day she touched at Naples. The bay was alive with small craft which seemed to dance lazily on the glittering Mediterranean. She was on Gordon Bennett's yacht, surrounded by all the luxury a rich American could invent.

A message reached Eugénie inquiring if she would receive the Duc d'Aumale, son of Louis Philippe. She had often danced with him in Madrid when his father was still on the throne of France and they had admired one another.

When he was taking leave of the Empress at the end of his visit, she accompanied him on deck.

He kissed her hand and looking up at her said: 'How lovely you were in those far-off Madrid days.'

The Empress, gazing out towards the far horizon replied:

'And you, Monseigneur, how handsome you were in those far-off Madrid days.'

Gradually, old age crept on, gracefully it is true, but irrevocably and it was always with a feeling of relief that she returned to Farnborough.

The Abbey which had held only four Premonstratension monks now sheltered forty Benedictines who had been expelled from Solesmes by the French Government.

How modern in her thought and way of life was this old lady! When these inventions were still a source of surprise and even

217

alarm to many of her generation, Eugénie ordered electricity to be installed at Farnborough.

Her motor car would arrive at the door daily, and she in filmy black, accompanied by one of her ladies, would step into it with the same alertness, as she did on that day, how many years ago, when she entered the golden coach on her way to her Civil Marriage in the Tuileries.

The Empress never admitted feeling fatigued; often her physician, Dr. Scott, would advise rest, but she only laughed and ordered her car for a longer drive.

The Empress Eugénie during one of her intimate conversations with Monsieur Palaeologue at the Hôtel Continental, December 1903, said that it was whilst she was Regent during the Austro-Italian War of 1857 that she first intervened in the government of France and henceforth, she never for one moment ceased to use her influence in public affairs.

How few people realized this, even to this day the name of the Empress Eugénie is linked with the Tuileries, Winterhalter and crinolines.

Later that afternoon, the Empress accompanied by a friend strolled under the arcades of the rue de Rivoli, suddenly an old man came up to her, his hat in his hand, and bowing low, said:

'A humble republican offers this bouquet to a very great Empress.'

Eugénie took the small bunch of violets and said:

'A humble old woman accepts it and thanks a very gallant republican.'

On another occasion, the Empress confided to Monsieur Palaeologue a story which illustrates the astuteness of the Duc de Morny.

The Emperor had been annoyed to hear that the Duc had placed a portrait of Queen Hortense in a conspicuous place in his drawing room, consequently Napoleon had asked Eugénie to approach the Duc on the subject.

The Empress talked with Morny and made him understand that the more he displayed his parentage, the less he would be treated as a brother.

The Duc seemed astonished and said: 'You told me just now that by placing the portrait of Queen Hortense in my *salon*, I have shocked the Emperor. Why should it shock him?'

It was a clever attitude to take, he did not admit that he was a bastard.

To my mind, the most pathetic incident recounted by Monsieur Palaeologue was when one day the Empress led him on to the balcony of her suite at the Hôtel Continental and pointing towards the Place de la Concorde asked him if he could see some steps leading out of the gardens.

'Yes, Madame,' he replied. 'That is where King Louis Philippe and Queen Amelie scrambled into a cab and fled.'

Then pointing in the opposite direction towards the Louvre, she continued: 'That is where I scrambled into a cab and fled.'

Much of the history of France is epitomized in those few words.

One of the friends of the Empress Eugénie returned from Cap Martin in the spring of 1906. The next day we lunched at Armenonville in the Bois de Boulogne in the wonderful atmosphere of a spring day in Paris.

He told me of the Empress:

'I had the honour of having *déjeuner* with Her Majesty; although the Villa is not very large, she lives in great luxury. Her servants, the food, the whole entourage recalls a Court.

'After our luncheon the Empress asked me to accompany her to a special terrace where comfortable arm-chairs were placed in a semicircle of flowering shrubs.

'The least breeze seemed to surround one with the scent of a thousand blossoms. Eugénie wore a large black hat:

' "I always wear this one," she said, pointing to her head. "The brim shades my eyes."

'Soft black suede gloves covered her still lovely hands as she opened her dark green parasol: thus we sat in her favourite corner.

'The weather was perfect and for a long time neither of us spoke.

'Without allowing her to see me, I watched the Empress. How beautiful she must have been. She seemed absorbed in thought, then presently she turned to me and said:

' "In a few days I shall be eighty. I am ready to go to rejoin those I love but there is still an unhealed wound in my heart – Alsace Lorraine."

'Once again we sat in silence, words were unnecessary.'

Paris was both looking and feeling grey one day when Sasha and I hurried to the Gare de Lyon to take leave of a member of the Russian Imperial family who was leaving for the South of France.

When we reached the station, the train was standing at the platform and attached to it was a portion of the Imperial train (this was before the days of the 'Blue Train').

The bedroom and sitting-room were filled with flowers and on the tables lay boxes of sweets and *petit fours* from Boissier and Marquis, the famous *confiseurs*.

The platform seemed crowded, the Russian Ambassador with all his staff, French Government dignitaries and high railway officials, were on the look out for the august traveller.

Suddenly there was a stir and Her Imperial Highness appeared; all moved forward bowing deeply to meet her.

After we too had paid our respects, I stood aside from the crowd; presently I saw coming down the platform what looked like a small procession.

Heading it was an old lady, entirely dressed in black enveloping crêpe veils, walking sedately, scarcely leaning on an ebony stick; she was erect and graceful.

Just a few people were grouped around her, four or five women and about the same number of men. Suddenly, I recognized the Empress Eugénie; as she stood taking leave of her companions, there was not a single station official in the group. Then she entered an ordinary *wagon-lit* with two ladies and a man; evidently her ladies-in-waiting and Pietri, her secretary.

As she leant out of the window saying a few last words to her faithful friends, the contrast between the two departures was almost overwhelming and tears came to my eyes.

Then there was a shout: '*En voitures, s'il vous plaît, le train part.*' A whistle and the train began to move. The Imperial Highness stood graciously acknowledging the reverences and deep bows of the assembly, all of whom were obviously hoping for a last glance from her.

I remained alone and as the last carriage passed before me, I saw the Empress still standing in her small compartment, a bouquet of violets in her hands. She looked at me and smiled as I made the deepest reverence of them all.

As the Empress grew older she seemed to regain her own nationality. Spain stood out before her eyes in all its charm. She knew that the Franco-Prussian War had been attributed to her influence but she refused to vindicate herself! Notwithstanding, she sorted and arrayed her letters and papers so that at some future date, if necessary, the truth might be revealed.

Then the greatest happiness came to her. On the day that France recovered Alsace Lorraine, silently she went to where all these documents were kept and burnt every one of them, saying: 'I have no longer any use for the past – the present suffices.'

Her journeys to the South of France had been interrupted by the First World War and now she resumed her visits to her villa.

She was ninety-three years of age. She dreaded the word DEATH. It is said, that once during her childhood, she had been forced to kiss the hand of the corpse of one of her father's old retainers. She refused to do so and even threw herself out of the window trying to escape the terror of the scene. This influenced her whole life. She realized her age, her blindness which seemed to grow greater every day, and also that she was becoming very weak and had not long to live.

However, she insisted that she wanted to go once more to Spain. The thought of her blindness preventing her from reading her cherished books seemed beyond her endurance.

So she went for the last time to her native clime.

As her blindness increased, she seemed to court more outside activities. She received the celebrities, the diplomats, academicians and artists. Sometimes she would entertain them for meals, at others when she felt too exhausted, she would see them for a few minutes in audience.

Then she consented to submit to an operation for cataract: it was successful and once more to her delight, she saw.

Her youth seemed to come back to her for a short time. Then the end came quite suddenly.

23 THE LIGHTS GO OUT

'We are drawing unknowingly and unconsciously towards the doom that lies in wait, with open jaws to engulf for ever, these human beings, young, handsome and filled with the love of life, on whom so much affection and care, both of body and soul, has been lavished by adoring fathers and mothers.'

Such were the thoughts which floated through my mind that night in 1913, as I sat watching Zoia, my daughter, dancing amidst a throng of young men and girls, in a sumptuous house in Paris.

They were waltzing to one of the finest orchestras. The men were choosing their partners for the Cotillon, and selecting their seats by laying a fan or glove on one of the gilt chairs ranged round the ballroom. In those days, men wore white kid gloves, and the girls long suede ones. Suddenly, Monsieur André de Fouquières clapped his hands and in his commanding voice cried:

'Prenez vos places pour le Cotillon.'

Then there was the flutter of pairing and finding their places. Sometimes, heart-breaking scenes occurred when somebody had pinched the glove or fan and was sitting on the selected chair, swearing that it had not been reserved.

Notwithstanding all these upsets, the signal was given, the strains of a waltz were heard. Baskets of favours appeared, carried by footmen.

Then the leader and his partner (it was always a great honour for a girl to be chosen for this), went round the room handing to each young woman a favour, for her to give any man with whom she chose to dance this figure, others were distributed for men to hand the ladies.

Monsieur de Fouquières would conduct the various figures.

In one, the men and ladies would draw coloured ribbons, then the leader would harness the ladies he had chosen ten abreast, and drive them with long gaily coloured reins winding in and out of the dancers, his partner doing the same with a team of men. At last, they stopped opposite each other, and detaching the harness

222

they would all float away waltzing with their opposite number.

Monsieur de Fouquières had an absolute genius for mounting these lovely figures.

The presents were sometimes very valuable, gold cigarette-cases, lovely fans, walking sticks, parasols, tie-pins and brooches.

How enticing, exciting and exhilarating, and yet how romantic it all was to hear the strains of a divine Strauss waltz, as one mounted the staircase leading to the ballroom.

There was so much poetry and yet there was always a certain anxiety beforehand, if one had not already been engaged for the Cotillon; if you had a partner it was sheer bliss.

And now, we come to the end of the Paris I knew, and the Paris of which my friends told me; it was the end of an epoch, the epoch of the 'horse-drawn' equipage, the age of elegance.

It has been said that Paris is a City of the mind, and that things of the mind are supreme in the world of men. I think that one could go further than that, and say that because it is the Capital of the European World, Paris has a unique gift to offer.

The City is so cosmopolitan, that she is able to absorb guests from every race and of every colour. She has a welcome for all and her spirit of toleration permits everyone to live their own life, and pursue their own customs, but in the end, her individual charm conquers their souls and they willingly absorb the culture of her accumulated wisdom.

No words can completely describe this City, each visitor finds the Paris he seeks. She is a city of the emotions, giving gladly and freely of her riches, to those who seek her hidden store.

To those who seek knowledge she opens the gates of her vast accumulation of learning, she is overwhelming in her bounty.

City of light, laughter and love, the pleasure seeker and savant enter within her enchanted walls, there to find their most fantastic dreams become reality.

Paris has witnessed the rise and fall of Empires and Kingdoms, of Princes and presidents, but she herself remains ever the same, gay and *insouciant*, but below her surface lie profound depths of thought and feeling – the accumulated wisdom of the ages.

Paris is just Paris.

Each day, each week, each month, the *tourbillon* of gaiety, if one could call it thus (it would be truer to call it lunacy), was sweeping all it encountered to heights of frenzy, soon to be flung and crushed against a wall of steel, helmets, guns and hatred.

Monsieur de Fouquières was leading more Cotillons, Grand Dukes gambling more wildly at Monte Carlo, 'bridge' assuming alarming proportions.

. Preachers were ascending the pulpit to damn the 'sins of society', the vices and scandals of the age.

Americans were introducing the habit of drink; for their use *les bars Americains* sprang up in the hotels and on the boulevards.

The art of love was becoming decadent, men no longer had time for love; *cocottes* had almost disappeared, tight-rope walkers and cabaret *chanteuses* were taking their place.

One or two women revived the era of the *demi-mondaine*, but they stood out, as by then there were so few.

Still, Monsieur de Fouquières led more Cotillons, still women seemed absolutely hypnotized by 'bridge' – the preachers redoubled their warnings, but the steel wall grew higher and we seemed to go joyfully to our fate.

Then, on 28th June, 1914, at Sarajevo, an Archduke died.

1920

The sun has risen, but the curtains of the state bedroom in the Palacio de Lira in Madrid are close drawn.

In the shadows of the great bed lies a still slight figure.

Nearly a century has passed since it first drew breath in a garden in Granada: but how truly has the gipsy's prophecy been fulfilled:

'You will be a Queen and you will live a hundred years.'

She has known the heights of power and has dwelt in the deepest shadow. Now as the bells chime for early Mass on a Sunday morning, Eugénie's soul takes flight.